THE DIARY OF A STROKE

THE DIARY OF A STROKE

Martin Stephen

Psychology News Press
London

First published in 2008
by Psychology News Press
9a Artillery Passage
London E1 7LN

psychologynews@hotmail.com

Cover: Sophie Clausen

Set in Garamond
by Keyboard Services, Luton
keyboardserv@aol.com

Printed in England by Biddles, Kings Lynn, Norfolk

Distributed by Melia Publishing Services
Godalming
Telephone 01483 869839
melia@melia.co.uk

ISBN 978 0 90763 3102

Contents

Prologue

The events in the following pages took place as described, to a real person and in real time, not so very long ago: two years and five months as it happens.

My purpose in writing this book, which is rather different from any of the other nineteen books I have written or edited, is the hope that it might save someone a little bit of the hell I and my family went through, and give them some hope.

Disaster

Day 1

It is 10.17pm, and I'm about to have a stroke.

It'll come as a complete shock. It's not exactly something I'm expecting. In common with millions of other people, I'm starkly ignorant. I know that a stroke is something to do with a blood clot, and that it leaves people unable to speak properly. What I really know about strokes is laughable. I'm about to be suddenly shoved down a very dark tunnel, and I'll have virtually no lights to show me the way out.

I'm Head or High Master of what is usually referred to as a 'leading independent school'. I'm attending the three day, annual conference of HMC, or 'The Headmasters' and Headmistresses' Conference', the professional organisation that represents a large number of leading independent schools. It's the last night of the meeting, and by hallowed tradition, it ends with a black tie dinner. I'm Vice Chairman (= one of yesterday's men: the Vice Chairman is simply the person who was Chairman the year before). As such, I have to give the vote of thanks to the current Chair for organising the conference. I've drunk very little, as I don't like drinking when I know I'm about to give a speech, even though it's hardly a formal address, more a vote of thanks. But when I stand

3

up and talk I like it to be me who speaks, for better or worse, not me plus alcohol. The speech is very short, adequate but no more.

The dinner ends at about 10 o'clock. I ring my wife to say goodnight, knowing that she as a Headmistress will have just got in. I tell her my day, and she tells me hers, as we have done over the years.

As I ring off, I have no idea that within a few minutes the potential definition of the man she married will change in the most dramatic manner imaginable.

Oblivious to what is about to happen, I find myself with an old friend who I've not seen for a year. He took a lovely overseas job as a Head, and as a result, I do not see nearly enough of him. He accepts my invitation to retire to the bar, and I order a round of drinks for him and a few other people I know.

I'm in my mid-50s and, with one exception, to all intents and purposes, am perfectly healthy. I'm probably a stone too heavy for my height, but I eat increasingly sensibly and have moved more and more to organic food in recent years. I go to the gym at least three times a week for an hour's work out, and walk the dog most days. I gave up smoking in my mid-30s, and in order to keep my weight down, I've stopped drinking except at weekends, and when I meet an old friend.

The one exception to my being perfectly healthy is that two years ago I was diagnosed with a serious cancer, and underwent radical surgery. It was only the second time I'd been in a hospital as a patient in my life. Surgery appears to have been successful, but when I go for my pre-med before the operation, my heart rhythm goes into overdrive. It's called atrial fibrillation; it means a frantically irregular heartbeat measured at times as over 160 beats a minute. It's probably stress-induced. I had the same symptoms a year earlier, and was told not to worry. The only reasonable conclusion is that my cancer has grown for a further year, having been misdiagnosed. Outwardly I'm calm. My heart tells the real story, though. Clearly, it's decided to panic.

For three days I don't know whether the anaesthetist will allow the operation to proceed, despite the fact that medication seems to have calmed down my heart. Anaesthetists are selfish creatures. It spoils their record if patients die whilst under their anaesthetic. Conversations take place that are positively surreal.

'If we operate,' the anaesthetist says, 'you may well die. If this fibrillation happens under or because of the anaesthetic, we'll never get you back.'

'If I don't operate,' the specialist says, 'you'll die.'

No pressure. Lots of choice there, then.

Only on the scheduled morning of the operation does the anaesthetist agree to the operation. They keep me waiting until the last possible moment before taking me to the theatre. Is it to test whether or not my heart will hold up under stress? I know what I think, but can't think it, because that will increase stress levels and that will...

This is plain daft, I think. From somewhere in me that I've only ever used once before, I summon a calm fatalism. I'm not in charge of this. My body, an anaesthetist and a surgeon have a grip on my life. They will decide whether or not I get back my own control over it. A sense of

5

calm, like the morphine that will take away the post-operative pain, descends over me.

Three weeks after the successful surgery my heart starts to beat irregularly again, not as seriously as before but still enough to leave me flushed and feeling unusually tired. The pattern is starkly predictable. I wake up with the fibrillation. I can sense it as I open my eyes. No pain, just a sense of disturbance. It lasts for two days, and then, my heart returns to normal. After that, the fibrillation returns every two or three weeks, but only for two days at most. I'm reassured to find out how many other people seem to suffer from an intermittent variable heartbeat; the most recent famous victim was Tony Blair. My position is simple; having been cured of cancer I've no intention of dying of heart disease. I ask to see a consultant. I am told he is a 'top consultant'. This worries me. The man who misdiagnosed my cancer was also a 'top consultant'. Of course, during the consultation my heart behaves perfectly. I'm given a monitor and wear it for the weekend. My heart continues to behave perfectly.

I've noticed a link between the irregular heartbeat and the combination of tiredness and alcohol, which the one book I've read on the subject tells me is a standard cause of the problem. Increasingly desperate to provoke a variable heart rate, I stay up very late and drink five glasses of wine. My heart refuses to take the hint. My reward for this advanced piece of medical experimentation is a searing headache next morning.

The consultant tells me I'm fine. The cancer consultant said much the same one year before I was diagnosed with cancer. I've not learnt from experience, and I believe the consultant. Nowadays, I throw away every shred of good manners I've acquired through my middle class upbringing. I fear that now I'm willing persistently to ask questions of even super consultants if I don't get answers. I know as I look back – that I'm alive because I forced a consultant into ordering a biopsy that he did not feel was necessary.

I also now know a number of other things I did not know then, minutes before I had a stroke.

A layman's version: atrial fibrillation allows the blood to circulate in the relatively large chambers of the heart – the biggest place the blood visits in its endless journey round the body – longer than is normally the case anywhere else. The result is an increased chance of clotting. One doctor tells me that the moment of greatest danger is when the heart actually stops fibrillation and returns to a normal rhythm. The return to normality fires the clot out of the heart like the ball out of a cannon. The cause of the stroke is a blood clot blocking an artery that supplies blood to the brain. There are other danger signs, as I found out afterwards. I'm a classic pear shape, and my blood pressure tends towards the high side, 140/90 usually being its best performance, and on the bad days the score is much higher. I've told myself that I suffer from 'white coat fever', the syndrome where a patient's blood pressure increases at the sight of a doctor. Whilst this has an element of truth in it, it is easier to believe this than it is to believe simply that my blood pressure is too high.

Stress? I defy any Head not to feel stress. In my case I've always viewed stress as something entirely natural (most animals spend at least some time in their life stressed out through either being chased or chasing, and my biochemist wife tells me we were designed for stress). I find out much later that medical opinion is seriously divided over whether or not stress influences a stroke. The balance of opinion among the consultants I'll be seeing for the next four months is that stress, surprisingly, isn't a factor in a stroke.

I will learn this, and much more, in the near future. For now, I'm sitting on a bar stool with my friend. The waiter has placed the drinks I've ordered on the bar, and I've paid. I take the change, make some silly joke with my friend and turn to pick the drinks up.

Suddenly, I feel a complete silence in my head. I watch, as if I'm a total stranger, my right hand sweep across the bar and knock the drinks into the lap of the barman. It is a technical exercise, seeing my hand wreak this damage. I've no control over my limb. It is as if it isn't mine, and in equally clinical manner, I notice a mixed expression of shock and embarrassment on the face of the barman. There's an embarrassed silence too from my friends, who start to look awkwardly at each other. I know that one of them is speaking to me, but I can only hear the voice as a dull rumble. It's as if I'm on a different planet, I just receive slightly fuzzy visual signals. In the words of my friend, speaking much later, it was as if I'd suddenly left the group, leaving my body behind.

I feel no pain, rather full-body numbness, as if a dentist's local anaesthetic had somehow seeped over my whole body. I know I'm being embarrassing, but in some way I don't understand, I've lost control of myself. I do feel embarrassed, horribly, grossly embarrassed. I don't want to make a fool of myself in front of these people with whom I work, these people who are my fellow professionals. It is imperative that I be by myself, that I shut a door, close out this horrible experience, sleep and wake in the morning to find it gone. It is as if I'm frozen.

I mumble something incoherent to the people who are with me. I'm trying to tell them that I'll be fine if I can get to my room, but they don't seem to understand me. There's something wrong, they seem to be saying.

Please take me out of here, I try to say.

Please take me away from all these other people who are now filling the bar, and who'll laugh at me and simply think that I'm drunk. *I must get away from the glare of people.* It is pride talking, shouting through what's happening to me. *I must not be seen like this.*

Somehow, mercifully, the message seems to get through. Willing hands and kinder faces grasp me firmly, hold me up. They're going to take me to the now-empty conference hall, next to the bar. Someone else, someone other than me, has taken over my body. I can't stand up, and know that the only reason I remain upright is the people holding me up. I know that I'm falling from side to side, but have no control over it, can only vaguely sense the pressure on me from those holding me up. The unpredictability of it is making me feel really sick.

Walking is almost impossible. Can I move that left foot forward? If I think very, very long, I think I can see it respond. But there's no strength in the leg, hardly any sensation even that the leg actually exists, least of all the feeling that it is still connected to my body. In effect I'm being dragged to the conference room, the nearest empty space, my toe catching precariously at the carpet. I'm taken into the cavernous expanse of the room where most of our talks have been given for the past three days; that room is now dimly-lit and empty. They've virtually packed up after the conference.

There's a single, incongruous table near the multiple doors through which we've just come, through which we've been filing for the last three days. Nearly all the chairs have been taken from it, there are five or six piles of them at the back, and the table is sitting in the middle of nowhere.

My sight is wrong. I can see the chairs – in an hour or so I will have multiple images every time I open my eyes – but now it is just that everything is blurred, foggy and seems to be moving up and down. Someone tugs at one of the chairs. It sticks to the one beneath it. But like the sword being drawn out of the stone, it eventually slides up and clear. It's brought to me, and I am helped to sit down.

A crowd of people gather around me. Five or six of them, in black tie, guests at the dinner. One is my friend. Two I vaguely know. Two – or is it three others? – are complete strangers. One of the strangers is extraordinarily kind. There's something in his eyes that tells me he knows what I'm going through, that he understands. He places his hands on me, supporting my left elbow as I'm guided to the chair. I note, or some part of me notes, that I can't feel the pressure of his hand on my elbow. I sit there, at the centre of a circle of people, stalling all conversation and action.

Disaster

A duty manager is called. He's a thin-faced man with a permanently worried look. He's genuinely concerned about me. He's human, after all. His instincts tell him, as they've told everyone else except me, that there's something seriously wrong with this customer. The duty manager does not want a death on his shift, or ill people being carted out of the conference centre. Although he's far too decent to say so, his training has told him that when somebody attending a conference falls ill, a wise manager sends that person over to the hospital. An ambulance is called.

My friends, and the strangers, stand around awkwardly. They're good people, but they don't know what to do. Someone brings a glass of water for me. I can't seem to hold it properly, can't drink it. Why does someone always bring a glass of water? The answer, of course, is that it gives them something to do, and allows a totally spurious feeling of having done something helpful.

I'm sitting there, like a latter-day Buddha, and of course, no sign of the frantic battle that is going on in my head is visible on my body. There's a part of me that knows exactly who I am and what I am. But my brain has been invaded by a fog of confusion; almost another personality is invading my space, stealing skills from me that I learnt as a child. I'm like the baby in the high chair who can't bring the biscuit to his mouth, and his limbs spasm out of his control. Who has dared take away the most basic and elemental marks of my adulthood?

Overwhelmingly, massively, *I want to be on my own*. I want to meet and, if need be, to fight this strange thing that has invaded my mind and switched off my body, putting a huge chasm between them. I don't want to be

11

with these other people, who are simply stopping me from focusing on something that I've got to do. But I don't really know what it is that I've got to do. Perhaps if I'm left on my own, if I can get to the sanctuary of my own room, I might be able to find out.

I've always been an obsessive personality. Now I'm obsessed with the need to battle whatever it is that has taken me over. It's overwhelming, so overwhelming that tears creep into my eyes. I want my wife to be here. Not just my wife. She has also been my best friend, from ever since we first met. And she will be asleep by now, quite unaware of what's happening to me. The frustration is appalling. I feel a mixture of exasperation and anger boiling within me. I can't share it with anyone, except my wife, even if I could find the words to express it. My speech is slurred, drunken. I'm asked for the phone number to ring my wife. I can't give it them.

My God! They'll all think that I'm drunk. I'll never be able to show my face among the professionals in my chosen field again. A drunkard, they'll think. The man who collapsed at the conference. A laughing stock. A joke.

The ambulance men arrive. There's a clear sense of relief among the others. I've no means of showing it, but my own alarm increases. I must not go to hospital. I can't go to hospital. If I go to hospital it'll mean I'm ill, that I can't make the absolutely crucial meeting I need to attend tomorrow morning. If only I can go to sleep it'll be all right. *I must be at the meeting tomorrow.* Suddenly, for the first time, the total seriousness of what's happening to me starts to dawn. If this is what I'm going to become,

Disaster

I can't do any job, least of all the one I hold and enjoy so much. I will be a cripple. There's no political correctness at moments like this.

One of the ambulance men is middle-aged, the other young. They look surprisingly like policemen in their uniform, and they huddle over me, kind and comforting, yet at the same time brisk and businesslike. They want to take me to hospital, but I know enough about the law to realise that they can't do that without my consent. I don't want to go to hospital. It'll mean admitting that I'm really ill. That I can't do. I mustn't be ill. I can't be ill. If I hang on in there, it will all go away.

Ambulance crews pick up the sins of the world, I think. Like social workers, teachers and policemen. They're paid to be there. Yet no one can pay someone to care. That bit has to be given from the heart. It comes from the human within us all, not from the bank manager.

The part of my brain that is still working perfectly, though forced into a corner, would also have been amused by how transparent the paramedics are. Were it not for my increasing sense of panic, I could see what I must look like to them. While I'm conscious they can't take me to hospital without my consent, so I must stay conscious at all costs. My feeling of panic increases. If I go to hospital what will happen to my job? If I can't work, what will happen to my wife and all our dreams for retirement? How about our grown-up children?

What about my employers? How can I ask anyone to support me if this is what I now am, a stuttering lump of flesh unplugged from the outside world?

The sense of isolation coupled with a sense of fear and

appalling loneliness is threatening to overwhelm me. For every unit of power that I generate, and try to see through to my body and mouth, only the merest trickle seems to arrive at the point of delivery. *I must focus.* If 99% of what I think isn't going to go further than the narrow confines of my skull, and is somehow aborted between desire and execution, I must choose a message of utter and stark simplicity, and focus simply on getting that through to those around me. Surely this nightmare world will go away if only I can be on my own and have the time to regenerate whatever it is that I've lost?

This is, of course, quite the worst path for the victim of a stroke to choose. But, of course, I don't know that, at my greatest time of need. I don't know, don't realise that I've had a stroke. It is essential for a stroke victim to receive immediate medical treatment. There are very expensive, and state of the art, centres in the United Kingdom that specialise in dealing with such emergencies. They can administer drugs and prescribe therapies that help reverse the effects of a stroke. Strangely, there is one near where I live. It is only open 9.00am to 5.00pm. One of the very few others in the country is near where I've been taken ill. Instead of being taken there, I'm taken to a local NHS hospital. Much later I find out it has a bad reputation. Was I taken there because the driver knew it would have empty beds? Does any NHS hospital have empty beds?

The 'normal' recovery rate from a stroke can be as low as a terrifying 10%. The outcome can range from catastrophic, leaving the person with no control over their bodily functions, and a paraplegic unable to speak but yet hearing and understanding everything, to the ideal, total recovery. And the chances of recovery can be dramatically increased if the patient is referred to a specialist unit within hours of the disaster. Millions of men and women don't know that, just as I don't. Millions of men and women aren't even able to recognise when they've had a stroke, as I wasn't able to recognise it.

I'm typical of many patients who, when they have had a stroke, spend precious hours fighting the truth instead of fighting the illness.

So I continue to deny what is happening because the truth is too stark and horrible to contemplate. Somehow I persuade those present to take me to my room in the conference centre. The duty manager fusses and fusses. There's a back route to my room, and if we take that nobody will see me. By now, I think he's seriously worried. His concern isn't for me, but for the reputation of the place. Someone has had a fit in his conference centre. The fact can't be ignored. It's a brutal reality, but it can be managed, if it is hidden away. I can hardly complain. His attitude is remarkably similar to mine. Manage the moment. Hide the truth. And anyway, I doubt it's really true. It's probably the fact of my anger clouding what little judgement I might have left, damning the man because hitting out feels good, takes the edge off the inner pain.

I'm helped along interminable corridors to my room, manhandled upstairs. No one sees us. The duty manager is pleased. I sit on the edge of my bed, just about managing to remain upright. The room seems strange, alien. Is it really where I have spent the last two nights? The world is swaying, though I know I'm sitting on the end of a

15

bed. I know if I fall over they'll take me to hospital, and they'll all think that I was simply drunk. Of course, what's actually happening is that my brain is frantically seeking to respond to the crisis that has plunged it, with remarkable lack of sympathy, into the need for major reprogramming. In this crisis, my consciousness is simply interfering, with fears about being laughed at and being unemployed, and all too human anxieties.

'Look', says the ambulance man, 'at least go for a check up. If there's nothing seriously wrong, I guarantee to get you back here by breakfast. What can you lose?'

He's a psychologist as well as a paramedic. Back by breakfast. What can I lose? Suddenly, his gentle and kind approach works. It's like a dam wall collapsing. My defences crumble. From some deeply buried reserve of common sense, I realise that I'm ill. This isn't a bad dream. It isn't something that will be cured by a good night's sleep. It's getting worse, not better. I can feel the world going greyer. This is a nightmare come true. Hours after my life has been permanently changed, I finally realise that this is one problem I'll not be able to cope with on my own. I've met my match, at least temporarily. I need to retreat to some corner of the boxing ring, and find somebody who'll tell me how to rearrange my brain within its battered cage.

All right, I mumble, slurring horribly. I'll go to hospital.

The duty manager's relief is almost pathetic to behold.

I'm manhandled, gently, back down the same corridors. They're darker now. More lights have been switched off. God knows what time it is in the morning. Is it my imagination, or do I have even less control over my limbs? Is it simply because I'm tired after so much exertion, or

16

that the ambulance men are more or less carrying me? Or is my situation getting worse even faster? I don't know, and an alarm bell is now starting to ring in my head, a tiny, flickering red light going off behind my eyes.

I'm put on a stretcher. It no longer matters to me as much as it did. I'm giving up.

I've never given up in my life. What's happening to me? Is this what happens when one is about to die? In order to die, does the victim have to give up the will to live? I hardly care any more, and ironically that worries me as much as anything else has this terrifying evening.

I'm loaded into an ambulance. I bounce as metal grates on metal. Something has deflated within me since I agreed to be taken to hospital. A part of me has gone, given up. I'm now just a package. I've ceased to be responsible for my own health. I'm fully awake, but my vision is more and more shaky.

Things are moving around and swaying, as if the ambulance was a boat. I lie on the stretcher as the doors clang shut. It's easier if my eyes are closed. The ambulance moves off, neon light fades from the cab, floods in again as we reach the road. The lights flick, flick, flick past me when I open my eyes. It's not irritating, surprisingly, but soothing, hypnotic. My friend has come with me and is sitting beside the stretcher. He smiles at me. I try to smile back. Only the right hand side of my mouth responds. I turn my head away, to face the metal panel. I can't turn my body.

Day 2

I'm in a darkened ward or reception area, on a trolley. I can only look up at the ceiling, which is featureless. Turning my head is hard now. A nurse has been to see me, I think. Taken a quick look at me and left. I seem to remember a doctor. No one tells me anything, and even my friend who is sitting beside the trolley, still in his black tie, can get no information.

By now it must be four o'clock in the morning, and I'm starting to feel nauseous. Irrationally, I'm worrying about the need to urinate. I don't feel as if my bladder is full, and I'm fretting about that. Why do I not want to go? I know that I can't walk, and I'm still in my evening dress. What will happen when I need to go to the loo?

There are vague noises, clatterings and mutterings, from other parts of the ward, but I can't raise my head and I'm still in a fog of ignorance about what's happening to me. Maybe I am all right. There is no sense of urgency now that I'm here, in this bloody hospital everyone was so keen on my coming to. Perhaps they don't think there's anything wrong?

Strange things start to happen in my mind. Amid all this quiet, I feel that the wise, the brave thing to do is to stay

18

silent, to be a 'good' patient, to cause no one any trouble. My friend gently reminds me that I really ought to let him ring my wife. I resist for half an hour or so. To call my wife will be another step towards admitting that this is something serious, and a stupid part of me is clinging on to the idea that it has all somehow been a dreadful mistake; it'll end as soon as it started if I don't do a thing.

Finally, even that resistance collapses, and my friend leaves me to make the call. How will he get through to her? I can't tell him the number. I hardly ever use the home one, and have never learnt my wife's mobile number. Why bother when it's so easy to hit the button on my mobile? Frighteningly, I am having trouble remembering my own mobile number. My anxiety level goes up several notches. Unknown to me, other friends have passed on my home number to him. But what if he rings? There is no phone in our bedroom. My wife never has her mobile switched on. One of our sons has fiddled with her mobile so that whenever she switches it on, it flashes up the signal, 'Good God! Mum's actually switched me on!' They have also made it read 'Yodaphone'. Yoda is Mum's favourite character from *Star Wars*. I'm rambling inside my head, losing it, I realise.

After too few rings the bloody answer phone will cut in. BT 1571. She won't hear it. I realise that, inside my head, I'm swearing a lot as well as rambling. Huge concern that my friend won't get through builds up inside me. I start to twitch. Suddenly it goes, and it's like after the cancer when they give you the morphine. Except I've had no medication.

Then someone does a ram-raid on my strange, artificial

sense of peace. Something is happening inside me that isn't good. I suddenly realise that my condition is deteriorating even faster. My symptoms, all of them, are getting worse. There's a fog inside my head now. My hands are shaking even more, my eyesight is worse, my speech is garbled, and the numbness on the left hand side of my face seems to be spreading. I'm starting to feel badly sick.

I wonder now if I was not suffering a second stroke. There is no medical evidence either way. I'll never know. Yet what if my first experience had been a harbinger for the real thing? What if it was a warning? What if someone had examined me, seen me, talked to me when I was first admitted? Would I have been spared all that was subsequently to come?

No medical personnel appear to be interested in me. I am in Accident and Emergency, but it is all Accident and no Emergency. Where I am is quiet. I worked as a hospital porter for two summer vacations as a student. I know the moments when a hospital or a ward goes berserk. There was always more noise than this on A and E. And twenty more staff would make no difference. But tonight there's a funereal calm. Is it *The Day of the Triffids*? Has some strange illness taken out all the other patients and staff?

My friend comes back. Where he walks from there is more light than there is where I am lying.

'Don't go to the light', I hear a voice say in my mind. 'Honey, don't go to the light'.

My brain has started to replay the film *Poltergeist* – where the little girl is taken in to a dream world, neither fully alive nor fully dead. The medium lets her parents talk to her. 'Don't go to the light', they plead with her. If she goes to the light, she'll die. My friend has come back from the light.

Reality bangs back in. 'I've rung her', my friend says, his hand on my shoulder, 'she's coming'.

I find out much later he's handled it marvellously. 'Martin's had some sort of seizure,' he told my wife, 'but he's still conscious. I think maybe you ought to come.'

My wife will be calm. She's always outwardly calm, whatever is going on underneath. My eldest son is staying with her at home, between flats. I know with absolute certainty that he will come as well and share the driving. I ask her later how she felt when the call came. She smiles a slight smile. 'What does it matter?' she says. According to my son, she was completely calm.

Suddenly, as suddenly as the stroke itself, the balloon that has been keeping me afloat collapses and is punctured. I feel myself spiralling down into a total loss of hope. For the first time, I let the word 'stroke' come into my mind. It must be something like that. I don't really know what a stroke is. I feel tears of self-pity and anger come into my eyes. A slurring, slumped heap of flesh in a wheelchair. That is what it has all come to. All that work, all that striving, all that fighting. For nothing. This is the future, and it is no future. I begin to wonder if there's any way that I can kill myself. Yet I'm stuck on a trolley, incapable of any controlled movement. This isn't a good place to try to commit suicide. Too many medics around.

I've not yet been given a brain scan, and no one has taken an electronic look inside my brain to see what has

The Diary of a Stroke

actually happened. I find out later that this is very bad news. The first thing a stroke victim needs is the picture of his or her brain taken. This will show where the lesions are, and if there has been a bleed into the brain. If I ever get to write a book about this, I tell myself, I'll demand that the first thing anyone does is to explain to the patient, exactly and in glorious Technicolor, exactly what has happened to them, exactly what *will* happen to them.

I'm moved into a different ward, and on to a bed. I've a vague memory of being moved, everything shrouded in the blue, dim neon of a darkened hospital. Curtains are drawn around me. I'm still in my socks, black trousers and dress shirt. The shirt is filthy, crumpled, rancid with sweat. A different nurse comes to see me, and a young doctor. They're bored, or tired, or both. I'm just another ill person, the nth of the long night. They ask very little, and say even less. I'm just a statistic.

I'm starting to feel very sick. It must be light outside now, but I can see nothing of it in the ward, which does not seem to have any windows to the outside. I try to keep my eyes closed as much as possible, because the sickness is a little more controllable that way.

I hear footsteps, my wife's voice. Should I feel joy, relief even? What I feel is despair. I can give her no hope. She and my loyal friend exchange a few words. He's had some sort of seizure, I hear my friend say again.

My wife swims into view. It is like looking through a prism. I see several versions of her face. Is this what an insect sees when it looks through its multi-faceted eye? I try to smile, but it'll not come. There are feelings within me I can't even identify: fear, love, shame at the trouble

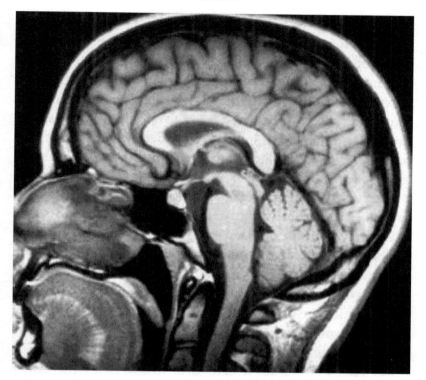

*Magnetic Resonance Imaging gives extraordinary sight – and insight –
into the structures of the brain. Stroke victims typically have a
number of 'tears' in the cortex caused by disruptions to blood flow.*

I'm causing, and intense loneliness. Above all, intense
loneliness. I can't even communicate with my own body,
let alone tell anyone else what's happening inside my
head.

My eldest son has driven with my wife to the hospital.
He stands by the bedside, looking serious and forlorn.
Why am I causing so much trouble to the people I love?
I can see the expression behind my wife's eyes. I know
what she's thinking. It's the end of our lives as we've

known them. We're neither of us fools. Close your eyes, she says to me. I learn later that my eyes are moving in two different directions, and she finds this horribly disconcerting.

As luck would have it, my middle son lives only a few miles away. After a while, my wife leaves me to tell my other son what has happened, and to ring my Chairman of Governors to tell him I am in hospital, with an accurate guess as to the diagnosis. The response is supportive, concerned. My wife is deeply moved. My friend has now gone to catch his flight, and he will be starting work later today having had no sleep. He's been lovely, right to the end. I can't remember what he said, as he went, I'll always remember how he said it. We're a maligned breed sometimes, we men. We can actually express emotion. It's just that sometimes we do it in a different way, by seeming to not say what we all know we feel and we mean.

My eldest son takes a taxi, goes to my hotel and packs up my room. Much later I realise what an appalling task he's been given. He has his own problems, his own worries. Now he has to take his father's on board. He pays the bill and picks up the car I have left in the hotel car park.

There will be two great revelations in my stroke, and one mini-revelation. I have the first one now.

From somewhere I remember my father speaking about stroke victims. He was a doctor, and now I think, rather a wise one. He was no great academic, but a man blessed with a very sharp brain and a totally intuitive diagnostic skill, something he passed on to my middle brother. I will, in the next few months, pass through more cathodes, electrodes and You-Need-Fifteen-Nurses, A-Surgeon, And-Enough-Electricity-To-Keep-London-Happy-For-A-month-Tests.

More procedures than I had ever dreamt existed.

What I will come to notice in these future months is the most important distinction of all. It is between those who smile at you with their mouths only, and say 'we'll just wait to see what the test results say', and those who purse their lips, wrinkle their brow and say 'I don't want to pre-judge the tests, but I'd be surprised if they didn't show...' Some medics make their mind up about what is wrong with you, take a tilt at a diagnosis, are not afraid of letting you follow their thought patterns. They trust you to understand that a diagnosis can change. Others feel they can only present you with the final, categorical, tried and tested conclusion. These seem to wait for the tests to tell them what is wrong with you. The problem is that the tests are usually inconclusive.

Medicine isn't an exact science, my father always used to say. He had also said to me, for some reason many years ago, that you always know those stroke victims who're going to get better. They fight it, they don't let it win.

This memory comes at me with the force of the snowball that you didn't know was coming crashing on your cheek. Why? Why has my brain, which increasingly I no longer understand and am rapidly losing control of, thrust this dim memory at me? Is the advice any use? Have I the strength left to fight?

'No' appears to be the answer.

My father was a GP, but his life led him beyond

medicine into activities which earned him a high media profile and, on the way, a knighthood. He became Chairman of the English Football Association, having been Chairman of Sheffield Wednesday FC in the days when they were a successful soccer club. My father brought the World Cup home to our house in Sheffield, to fly out with it next day to the 1970 World Cup, where England played as the reigning world champions. My father fired Alf Ramsay as England team manager. At least to me, his youngest son by a large margin and therefore the one who knew him least well, he had more integrity and certainty about himself than anyone I've ever known, except perhaps my father-in-law.

I suspect his success in the areas that earned him his knighthood owed a huge amount to the fact that, whilst he enjoyed what he did as a doctor and what he did additionally, his ego never made him dependent on his status. This man I was at last getting to know properly died in a hospital ward, my last vision of him being surrounded by chits of nurses calling him by his first name, hooked up by rubber tubes to steel and chrome machines, in an alien environment, a man drowning in machinery as well as the revolt of his own body. As with my mother's death, there was no dignity there.

I am pretty sure that as soon as he had that first attack he was to all intents and purposes a dead man. How wonderful if he could have died at home, the classic Victorian scene, with his family gathered round his bedside, instead of in the noise and bustle of a hospital ward with that same family continually being moved aside to see if a drip needed to be changed. Perhaps I'd blocked out all this from my mind as being a little too close to home.

I must be tired now, because things are fragmenting. My wife is there again. I mumble, gesture for something to be sick into. A cardboard, kidney-shaped vomit bowl is placed by my mouth. Its surface is rough. I start to be violently, rackingly sick. It is last night's meal, lumps of undigested meat. I seem to fill the bowl. Seconds later, the sickness returns, and I throw up again. Then again. Surely there can be no more food left? Being sick is now actually painful, and I'm retching, going through muscular spasms that bring up no more solid matter. There's a foul taste in my mouth, and I start to whimper. *Oh Christ,* I'm saying in my mind, *I just can't do this, I just can't cope.* Is this what torture victims in the Middle Ages used to feel? Please, someone, anyone, make this stop.

When I open my eyes I have double or treble vision. I try to raise my left hand, and place it on the left-hand side of my face. I've no sensation at all on the left-hand side of my face. Is that why my speech is so slurred? Is it that I can't move my lips on the left-hand side? Or is it that part of my tongue is disabled?

A young doctor comes to see me. The earlier ones made fleeting visits, wanted to know very little, seemed content to merely note how I was without saying much or doing anything. This one is more focused, her manner medical. She wants me to push with my feet against her hands, and then push with my hands against her hands. I can do this a bit. I'm strangely heartened. This is something I can do better than I could before. I can actually feel my legs exerting the pressure, can actually control them and make them push. This is better. I can see that she is pleased with what I'm doing, though she doesn't tell me so. I'm full of an overwhelming desire to please the doctor. She is very cold, going through the routine of the examination with clinical precision, a screen behind her eyes rather like the cellophane on the display screen of a new mobile phone. Perhaps they're both there for the same reason, that screen stopping her brain being scratched by emotion.

Why do none of the people who see me in this place treat me as if I have a brain? I feel the stirrings of battle within me. Maybe I can fight this thing. Maybe all isn't lost. After all, I can push with my feet. A bit.

I'm wheeled on a trolley for a brain scan. Nobody tells me what's happening, and it is only later that I find out. My wife knows, but doesn't say a word. There are two types of stroke. If the blood clot breaks the wall of the artery, the blood leaks into the brain. All hell is let loose. Bye Bye. The parrot falls off the perch. Curtains. There's a medical name for this type of stroke, which is, in effect, a haemorrhage. The other type of stroke releases no blood into the brain. It is a blockage, not a breakage. It fries certain neural pathways in the brain, but the brain can eventually re-route those pathways.

No one talks to me, no one explains anything. I'm becoming used to seeing nothing but ceilings, polystyrene tiles and neon lights. I go back, or am trundled back, to the ward. It feels strange lying on a trolley, being wheeled by two men, looking up at neon-lit ceilings. I am disembodied. Other people rush by, determinedly not

looking at The Patient On The Trolley. Hospitals are full
of people heading firmly somewhere else.

I receive a regal visitation. The Consultant. I never
really learn what his specialisation is. He tells me, with
that wonderful sense of power that many consultants
have, that the scan is good. It looks like there has been
no leakage of blood into the brain. I don't yet know the
difference between the two types of stroke. I don't know
yet that the scan has taken quite an alarmingly long time,
and that the reaction of this very well-meaning NHS
hospital to a stroke victim has been rather too slow and
methodical. I call the consultant The Fat Consultant, after
The Fat Controller in the *Thomas the Tank Engine* books.
He's ample, benign, laughs a lot. He's loving it. He's an
actor. This ward is his theatre, I and the students his
audience. We are both captive, in our different ways. He
tells his students all about me.

Hello, I want to say, and put my hand up. Here I am.
It's me. You know, me. Not just a patient. Almost a
human being. Could you please tell me how sick I am?

There is a brilliant section in R.D. Laing's *The Divided
Self* where he dissects a section of Kraeplin on schizophrenia. Kraeplin, the man who identified schizophrenia
as a disease, was 'presenting' the patient and, Laing
argued, totally de-personalised him.

Kraeplin's patient sits with his eyes shut and pays no
attention to his surroundings. He does not look up even
when he is spoken to but, eventually, he answers, beginning
in a low voice and gradually screaming louder and louder.
When asked where he is, he says 'You want to know
that too. I tell you what is being measured and is measured

29

and shall be measured. I know all that and could tell you but do not want to.'

When Kraeplin presses him for an answer, the bad and mad patient ignores the good doctor. But now Kraeplin loses his rag. 'How can you be so impudent?' the flabbergasted doctor inquires.

The attitude hasn't changed much. I am an object on view. But what about the future? Will I still have a job after all this? What's my prognosis?

My bit part over (shown to strut and fret my few seconds on the stage), the Fat Consultant and his entourage leave. Job done. Specimen A displayed. They don't ask me if I have any questions. After all, lumps of meat are there to be consumed, not spoken to. Anyhow, I'm not in much of a state to ask them anyway.

There's a growing feeling of strength; not in my body, but in my mind. I'm receiving a mass of conflicting signals from my body, the body that will no longer obey the simplest instructions. Yet I know that somehow I'm the same person who ordered those drinks at the bar what seems like years ago. I'll never try to drink a Jack Daniel's again. If my brain is OK, surely my body can learn to do the basic things again, as it did when I was a child?

I realise that I must look like death, and sound even more like it when I'm gut-rottingly tired. I'm starting to contemplate the possibility that I'll get better, but I've no real way of telling my family that, no real faith to give credibility to my words. Actually, I'm doing a classic stroke thing, as I find out long afterwards, and suffering multiple mood swings. The hospital keeps trying to treat me as an invalid, somebody for whom the best treatment is to be wrapped in a blanket and left to fall asleep. You are a good patient, for those who work in a hospital, if you stay in bed. Some instinct tells me that I must force the issue and push myself to the very limits.

In my previous Headship there was a man called Ian Bailey. He had been a pupil at Manchester Grammar School, returned there to teach and left only to fight a good war in a Scottish regiment. When I knew him, he was in his 80s; he was once described as 'the soul of the school'. 'Basher' Bailey denied his nickname totally. He was one of the gentlest, most generous and lovely men I have ever known, though that gentleness had a core of steel. I bumped into him one evening after I had been battling to raise money for bursaries, and was feeling as bruised as my audience. He grinned at me. I must have looked surprised.

'I knew it,' he said, 'I knew it when I first met you. You're a fighter.' He meant it as a compliment, I think. As for me, I'd willingly have given up a lot of the fights my career and private life have given me, but Ian was right. Or had been, until this ... thing happened to me. I find myself thinking about my own father, my father-in-law and Ian, in a confused maelstrom of memories.

Fight? Or give in? There's a male nurse on the ward. He's loud, vulgar and funny. He, and everyone else who comes to see me, is clearly expecting a slow recovery, or none at all. I mutter to myself in the bed, angry with him and his acceptance of my disability, angry with myself. I want to tell him how wrong he is. The primary point of contact with other human beings is speech. Mine is

31

slurred, though the lack of feeling on the left-hand side of my face is starting to go.

It is a turning point. Without quite realising, I start to fight again, concentrating on that one area of speech.

If I can speak properly, people will be less inclined to think that I'm a cripple. I start to mouth words, wrapping my lips and tongue around the sounds as if they were the best delicacy in the world. If I think really, really hard, the words come out sort of clearly. It takes a massive amount of effort to do this. The brain works faster than the mouth, lips and tongue. It leaps ahead with the ideas, but leaves the execution a long way behind. You have to slow yourself down, think ahead of each sentence and sometimes each word that you wish to speak. You sound like a cross between a pompous politician and Sir Laurence Olivier. But it works, and whoever else you may sound like, you don't sound like an idiot who has lost his mind.

So speech must be the first target. But surely the key word is 'target'? I'm starting to fight back. I'll not cure this bloody thing overnight. I must set myself targets that will stretch me to the very limit, but are doable. I'll not walk today, that much is clear.

Or ever again, a little whispered voice says inside my head.

I tell the voice to shut up. Of course I'll walk again. Of course I will. But today, I must concentrate on talking and putting some semblance of control back into my arms and hands. If I reach out for something, my hand takes a sideways, looping swipe at it, just as it did at the hotel bar the night before. I must concentrate on that hand, slow it down and stop it scything through space.

I confess a lust for chocolate to my wife. I plead with her to buy me some. She goes out and comes back with Smarties. She puts some on the table at the end of the bed, spread out. 'Reach out for it,' she says. 'Pick it up.' I try. *It is like shove ha'penny.* Finally I get one, find my mouth and cram it in, crunching. Smarties: I love you. As for my wife, I feel a deep hostility.

I can do something about my sight as well. If I pay a vastly inflated amount, I can buy a card that will let me watch television. I thought the NHS was free at the point of contact, but apparently you can travel first or second class within it. Shouldn't every patient be able to watch TV, not just those who can afford it? My wife and children have bought the card for me. My vision is still bad and I can't watch it. I look at the fluorescent light in the ward, and I see two, perhaps even three images of it. I learn to switch the television on, and move my eyes suddenly to the fluorescent light. Is it my imagination, or is the light starting to merge into one unit the more I do this?

My wife and my children are lovely, staying by the bedside and not revealing any of the boredom they must feel. My eldest son has to return to London. My wife asks me to keep my eyes shut. When I open them, they still roll around in a manner that clearly disturbs her.

Trying to feed myself is a disaster. I'm wrapped in the plastic that covers the bed and try to pick up some food. It's hopeless. The spoon goes to the top of my head, not my mouth. By the time I steer it down to my mouth most of the food has fallen off the spoon *en route*.

I make a vow to myself. I'll make them give me a

Zimmer frame tomorrow morning. Before my wife visits, I'll somehow get to the shower. I'll have a shower. I'll shave myself. I look at the hands that can't even pick up a spoon with any certainty. Tomorrow, they'll not be back to normal. But I'll make them do at least a little of what I require.

My wife and the boys have left. The son who lives locally has done more than his stint, turning up to see his ill dad, the expression on his face saying it all. But now my personal support team have all gone, and I'm alone with my illness. The hospital starts to go to sleep. I'm terrified that I'll lie awake, remembering the endless nights tossing and turning after cancer surgery. But suddenly, after 24 hours of Hell, there's the tiniest glimmer of heaven. Perhaps I can make it better. Perhaps there's a future. I'm going to fight this. Clutching that precious thought to my brain, it is as if there's a gently warming hot water bottle inside me. To my surprise and immense pleasure, I fall asleep.

Recuperation

Day 3

Days start and end early in a hospital ward. By 6.30 am there are stirrings and noises, clattering and bangings, and I'm awake. I feel strangely calm. The night has not been the Hell I expected it to be from my cancer surgery. I've actually had some sleep, and not lain awake all night.

The bed clothes are rumpled, and my surgical gown wet with sweat. My wife will come about nine o'clock, I know. I must, I absolutely must, show her a member of the human race by nine o'clock. This presents a serious problem. I look awful. My face is covered in stubble. I stink. This is partly because I've been sweating like nobody's business, partly because nobody has thought to change the surgical gown in which I'm dressed.

Why can't I remember having my clothes taken off me?

If I open my eyes for too long, they start to swivel in opposite directions. I can't walk and I'm far from sure that I can even manage a Zimmer frame. Yet I must, must get to the shower room. I must clean myself up, and in so doing, perhaps rinse away some of the horror. I swing my legs out of the bed. The world is revolving now, as if I'm at sea in a very heavy swell. I wait a minute, hands pushed down hard on the mattress, as they were only a few hours ago in my hotel room.

The Diary of a Stroke

Suddenly I'm aware of the hospital ward, as if every sensitivity I possess has been suddenly given a power boost. There are the square neon lights, perfect amid marching, dirty polystyrene square tiles. One of the two tubes in a light is fizzing and flickering. It'll stay that way until I leave the ward. The steel beds are grey, the covers over the three other beds are grey, and there's no colour in the ward at all. It is as if we are all grey men, declining into a grey future, grey lives and a grey death.

If I stare hard at the exit sign, the two squares of grey background and yellow light of the letters come together until there is maybe half an inch between them. I need to concentrate to bring the two images together, and it hurts badly, a strange sharp pain in the eyes, if I do it for too long. Opposite me is an older man who never seems to wake up, and lies slumped in the bed until the nurses move him. He moans all the time, whether he's awake or asleep. Next to him, by the window, is a figure who I can't see under the blankets. He does not move. By my side, nearer the window, is Mr Frankland. I don't know why I know he's Mr Frankland. He's 80, and confused. Every half an hour or so, he swings his legs out of the bed and marches purposefully to the door. He stands there, looking authoritative. Then, he goes back to his bed.

The floor is grey, shiny. It has a thin smear of muck all over it, where the orderly's ineffectual mop has rearranged the surface dirt. Earlier my wife had washed my locker, first removing the previous occupant's empty crisp packets and rubbish. There is still a pile of grey and black fluff on the floor in the corner by the locker, and something that looks like a thin slick of dark grease.

Both will remain there for the duration of my stay. There are tubs of antiseptic hand wash every few yards in the ward and the corridors. Notices scream the dangers of MRSA at anyone who can be bothered to read them. And here is a pile of grey and black fluff on the floor in the corner by the locker, and a thin slick of dark grease. This is my ward. At the moment, it is my world.

If I sit up, with my legs over the edge of the bed, and clench my fists and stick them ramrod straight down the side of my body, so they jam hard into the mattress, I can keep myself upright. I feel the pressure alternately, first on one fist and then on the other, as my body tries to lean first one way and then the other. It's as if some huge, tidal force is pressing down on me, first to the left, then to the right. If all I can do is manage to sit upright, and that only with great difficulty, how will I ever be able to walk?

There's a Zimmer frame by the bed. I've not asked for it. I suspect it has either been parked there, or perhaps was used by the previous occupant of the bed.

If I use the frame both my hands will be on it. Yet my sponge bag is there in the bedside cabinet, brought by my wife, and the bathroom will be useless without it. I have no hands spare to carry anything.

Imagine this is a challenge, I think to myself, set by an alien species to decide if humanity is really an intelligent species. Or an exercise of the type the Army and Navy use to choose officers. There's the sponge bag, Object A. There's a cripple, Object B. There's the bathroom, Object C. Object B has to use his brain to work out a way of getting Object A to Object C at the same time as, and in the company of, Object B.

The Diary of a Stroke

Right.

My surgical gown is tied, or not tied, at the back, and reveals my backside to any passer-by. If this happens on my way to the bathroom, it'll destroy any residual dignity I might possess, and probably not do much for anyone, human or alien, who witnesses the sight either. The alien might not understand this particular sensitivity whereby humans tend to mind who they allow to see such a vision, but it happens to matter rather a lot, particularly to a casualty whose dignity has been sorely damaged in recent hours.

My belt is on top of my locker! Heaven knows how it got there. My hand swings over it, like the crane poised over the goodies in a fairground machine. Finally, I manage to make contact, clutch at the belt fiercely.

I fumble at the belt, finally manage to hold it with my right hand. I am left-handed. It feels odd. My left-hand side seems worse affected by the stroke. I bring the belt over to the bed. I can't reach behind to tie the surgical gown properly. As far as my hands are concerned even to try would be a joke. But if I look down between my legs I can see the two halves of the gown. I finally manage to grab both of them. I try an extraordinary bouncing movement on the bed, yanking at the two halves of the gown. I manage to get my bottom off the mattress just enough, at about the third try, to allow the two halves to come together. But the co-ordination is wrong. The brief moment when the cloth is free to move does not coincide with my frantic yanking at the cloth. I finally manage to move the two halves at the eighth or ninth bounce. I can put the belt on the bed and push it round behind me. I gather it together. I can't get the leather into the buckle for ages. When I finally manage it, the pressure of the belt holds the two halves of the gown together. Dignity is secured. But it's more than that. Now I can drop the sponge bag down the front of my chest. It stops where the belt hugs my waist. I'm carrying my sponge bag, like a deformed child conceived in my lower chest. Remember *Aliens*. Will my sponge bag seek to burst out at any moment from my chest? Right. Baggage secured. Parcel in the hold. Now there's the problem of the flight.

I reach out, nearly toppling over in so doing. I grab hold of the thin metal, and try to drag the Zimmer frame towards me. Its feet are insulated with some non-stick substance, to stop it slipping on the floor. It drags as I try to pull it, squawks nastily, starts to tip over. I try to correct the imbalance, and ram the thin material back on the floor. Finally, I've a Zimmer frame roughly in front of me, both my hands resting on it. I inch my bottom forward on the mattress, and feel my feet on the floor. It's cold.

This I can do. I know I can still push with my feet. About the only thing the medical fraternity have asked me to do is push against their hands with my feet. *It's OK. He can push with his feet. He's had a stroke, he's going to walk around with crutches for the rest of his life, he'll never speak straight, but he can push with his feet.*

Stop babbling.

If I push up I'll be standing. I'm breathing too fast. I push. The world takes a staggering lurch. I grip the Zimmer frame so hard that my knuckles turn white and I feel actual pain. I'm clutching too hard, tilting the frame over. A few more inches and I'll topple along with it. I correct with my other hand, over-compensate. But the frame straightens.

I'm standing up. I should feel good. Instead, I feel terrified.

Is it six months or a year when a baby stands up? I'm celebrating doing something I've taken for granted for 56 years. And I'm not doing it very well.

Now the real challenge. No one has seen me on the ward. This is the interesting thing about being an NHS patient in an NHS ward, another part of my mind tells me. The people here are lovely, charming. But I've no sense of anyone knowing who I am, let alone what I'm in hospital for. There's a routine, a system. Observe that, and all will be well. And the patient? He or she will be treated kindly enough, as far as time allows. But the system is all important. Observe the system – for example, drugs will be administered at 9.00pm, not when this infuriatingly individual patient might actually need them – and then observe your own needs. That might mean gathering at the Nurses' station and giggling or laughing as some patients try to sleep.

Six months later, I'll find myself by my wife's bedside as she recovers from keyhole surgery to her knee. It is a small, private hospital, and for the same number of patients, there are nearly half the staff. Yet the care is phenomenal. It is as if the nursing staff in this hospital are absolutely and totally focused on the patients to the exclusion of anything else.

The reverse is the problem in my NHS hospital. The staff spend time with each other, not with the patients. They gather together to talk far too often, as if cuddling together for moral support. They joke, and flirt, with each other; almost as if they're the actors on stage and the patients the captive audience. Too much of their attention is focused inwards, on them, not outwards to the patient. The patients come and go, it is as if they're saying: *We, the staff, are here all the time. This is our world, where we work. You the patient may join our show, but only as an observer. This is our theatre, and it is run for us more than it is for you.* These aren't bad people. Indeed, they're rather lovely people to meet on the street. But the culture is wrong. It isn't a culture of service, not even a culture of dedication. It is a job, and the chance to joke with one's mates is a great relief from the tedium. As for the patients, too many of them are old and infirm. They'll push the emergency button because they want someone to pay them attention, not because they're undergoing a cardiac arrest.

Maybe that's why no one has shown me where the emergency button is.

It's still early. I must make it to the bathroom. Before they stop me and tell me I can't, like the nurse did last night. She wouldn't let me get out of bed, and my wife couldn't hold me up.

Before they wrap me in a blanket and tell me to go to sleep, I've enough residual common sense to realise that it would be madness, utter stupidity, to take a shower, desperate though I am to do so. I can hardly stand touching the Zimmer frame, and there will be nothing to hold on to in the shower. If I fall and break a leg, an arm or a hip, then I'll be truly done for. Yet this can't hold me back. I must not be dominated by fear or I'll never get better. I'll try for a compromise. I'll try to make it to the bathroom, wash myself down by the basin and shave off my stubble. It's like it was in the bar, when all I yearned for was to get to my room. The room would be a haven, privacy. Being on my own would make everything all right. So it is now. In the shower room, in some strange way I'll be all right. If I can get there.

I look at the Zimmer frame, and I feel scared. Cautiously, I try and move one foot forward. It works. I order my other foot to move forward as well. It does so, slightly less willingly. I've made two steps. Or one and a half. I feel triumphant. Now I must move the Zimmer frame forward, and repeat the whole exercise. I know from somewhere that I have to keep my feet right within the frame. Strange. It's not the sort of information I usually have to hand. I'm now four paces away from the bed. I feel like a sailor losing sight of land. The whole perspective of my life has been reduced to my distance from a hospital bed. The swaying has not stopped, but it is like a regular rolling sea now, lifting me up and down in a predictable pattern.

I look longingly back at the bed. There is safety, comfort. I learn that I need to plan my stumbling steps within the rhythm of this rolling sea. The foot must move forward on the upswing, and must at all costs be grounded by the time the downswing comes. Two, three, four more paces. I'm now at the door of the ward, and starting to feel sick. A ward orderly passes me, and I smile at him. He's not going to turn me back! He smiles back, and moves on. He's a new orderly. He knows nothing about me, least of all that I'm a menace on metal, unsafe flesh in charge of a Zimmer frame.

Mercifully, the bathroom is only a few feet from the ward

door. I know that. I'd asked my wife for a description of the corridor outside the night before. I start to shake. It's fear as much as anything muscular. I'm scared, more scared than I've ever been in my life. I'm stranded, marooned. The bed, my haven and my safe harbour, is behind me and out of reach. My destination is six massive double steps away. Am I to fall down, and become a package yet again, a brown paper parcel to be sent back to bed?

From somewhere I gather new strength. The shaking subsumes in to a faint trembling. Each step is an individual achievement, like reaching the peak of a hill. I feel a bead of sweat start to roll down my forehead, become entangled in my eyebrows. It drips into my eyes, stinging. I hardly notice. I must hurry, before someone sees me. In my hurry, I misjudge the angle of the Zimmer. It bashes into the side of the door, and gets stuck. I have to reverse somehow, swearing under my breath at the unfeeling, hollow metal frame and my own inability to do even the simplest of things. Finally, I make it through the door of the bathroom.

I've a replaced one sanctuary with another, a bed for a bathroom. I take a few moments to rest and recuperate. There's a sink, a mirror and a long pull for the light. There's also another pull for emergencies. I note it cynically. That is the one to avoid at all costs. I take my wash bag from the top of my gown, reaching down for it through the neck with my left hand. I'm still holding on to the frame with my good, right hand. In withdrawing the bag, I drop most of its contents into the sink. Thank God, none of them go onto the floor. I simply could not bend down to pick them up.

As carefully as my ever-wandering hands will allow, I

45

put the spilt items back into the wash bag. Or rather my swooping hand hovers over them, like the crane over the goodies in a fairground game, and I grab whatever I can. I leave out the shaving foam and the razor, a disposable, three blade Gillette. First, throw water on my cheeks. My hand, which belongs to somebody else, throws the water everywhere, and some of it lands on my face. Right. Minor victory. Now the foam. I squeeze it onto my left hand. The hand is shaking. I order it to place foam on either side of my face. It will not go where I want it to. It smears the foam on my left ear, zooming past my face. I squeeze out more foam. I order my hand even more strongly to spread it on my face. When I concentrate, harder than I've ever concentrated, it moves vaguely towards my face and I splash the foam even more faintly in the right direction. Some of it goes up my nose, and I sneeze violently. That stings too.

At least that bit is still working. The nerves in my nose. At least I missed the eyes.

If I allow my concentration to lapse for a part of a second, the hand goes all over the place. Yet at the end of this silly battle with my mind and my limbs, the bits I can shave are covered in the foam.

Now comes the hard bit. Can I trust this wandering, wavering hand of mine to bring three sharp razor blades to my face? 'No', is the honest answer. An image flashes in to my mind, the face in the mirror the last time I cut myself shaving. For some reason I'd moved the razor sideways, not down. Pink flesh, stark white shaving foam, flecked with blood pulsing through. But I've got to do it. I hold the razor in my left hand. It feels normal, until I try

46

to move it. Then it twists and turns in my hand, as if I am holding a snake. In unity there is strength. I place my right hand over my left hand, and seek to guide the razor that way. It hovers over my left cheek. Here goes. I plunge it down. It moves downwards, rather than in a sideways slashing move, and a swathe of facial hair is removed.

I repeat the experiment laboriously for each razor stroke. Only once do I make a mistake. I can't resist the urge to do a sideways, slashing stroke of my hand, and I open a cut just under my chin. It's far from a perfect shave. My face looks like a harvest field through which a drunkard has driven a combine-harvester. It's the best shave of my life.

I realise something remarkable. I've actually been standing with both hands off the Zimmer frame. It was when I steadied the razor with both hands. I did it unconsciously, and, somehow, my body compensated. As I realise what has happened I lurch forward, spill the razor into the basin, grab hold of the frame with both hands. But I'm smiling. *I've stood up properly, even if only for a few seconds.*

That's my face done. But now there's the rest of me, unwashed since the damned thing first happened, and stinking of sweat. I undo the belt and shrug forward to drop the gown to my feet. I've worked that one out. I can plonk myself down on the loo seat, and that will bring my hands close enough to pull the gown up. But that's for later.

I'm standing stark naked in the bathroom, and my gown is dropped by my feet. My legs are shaking now, quite badly. I've pushed the frame to one side, to get nearer the sink, and I'm leaning hard on the sink edge, rather than the frame. I hope it's secured properly to the wall. To turn the tap on I must take my left hand in my right hand, and let the right hand guide my left hand to the metal. Thankfully, it's a disabled tap, a great long lever sticking out over the basin. I don't actually have to hold it, just bash at it.

Using both hands I turn on the hot water, and then the cold. Soon I've a basin full. Luxuriously, I soap my hands and let them smear a lather wherever they can reach. I'm swaying forward, and twice bash my knuckles hard on the sink. I've a brief image of my knuckles sliding up the soap-smoothed side of the sink, and of my falling over. I don't care. I feel so proud of myself. I wet a flannel, splashing water all over where I hope the soap has gone. I'm wet now, and there's a pool of water on the floor. The warmth is going, and my body starts to feel chill, but that is also invigorating, like a cold shower.

I try to brush my teeth, but the brush will not go up and down, or sideways, but insists on stupid, swooping diagonal strokes. Just as the razor did. I bash my gums twice, hard. They don't bleed, but they hurt. At least I can feel them, even the blow on the left-hand side. The taste of the toothpaste is wonderful. I can feel the fur being scrubbed from inside my mouth.

I look at my face in the mirror. It's grey, like my hair. My face is lined, my eyes very tired, great bags under them. They are not focused, and for the first time I see them wander. My hair is lank, greasy. The world is still going up and down like the flight deck of an aircraft carrier in a gale. But if I sit on the loo, I can bend my head forward into the shower cubicle, and maybe even wash my hair. Now that would be a real bonus. I'd not really even dared to imagine I might stretch to a hair wash. But I can imagine myself soaking the floor.

I sit down on the loo seat, landing with a bang. I grab the gown, place it carefully in the wash basin. It's wet there, but it's going to get even wetter on the floor. I check there's shampoo in my wash bag, and lean forward. My head wants to carry on forward despite the fact that I'm telling it to stop. It collides with the up pipe on the shower unit, and it stops. It hurts, a lot. No, this is silly. The water will either come out boiling hot or freezing cold. I withdraw my head, and reach out to the flat handles to turn the water on. Again I realise why disabled taps are fitted on the units in hospitals. They're wonderful. I can't wrap my hand round them, but I can bash at them until the water is running tepid. I stick my head under it, and feel it rush through my hair, beat at my eyelids and threaten to run up my nose. It is a glorious, wonderful feeling, and I stay there under the rushing water far longer than is necessary. I withdraw my head, and squeeze the shampoo container, forgetting for a moment the state I'm in. My shaking hand drops the container, but not before a trail of white shampoo has been left on the floor.

I feel like crying. I'm beginning to notice that I'm subject to serious mood swings, exaltation one minute at the conquering of some minute task, depression the next at some tiny failure. I manage to control my mind. The shampoo has skidded across the floor, but if I stretch I can just about reach its tip. The towel is near me. I cast it over the shampoo bottle, and draw it towards me. Finally, it is in my hand again, my right hand.

More slowly this time, I squeeze shampoo into the

palm of my left-hand. I raise my hand, as I've done countless times in my life, to rub the shampoo into my hair. I spoke too soon about missing my eyes. I nearly poke my right eye out, and manage to put shampoo into it. Scrabbling around with my right hand, I grab the towel and scrub at my stinging eye. When the pain is less, I pick up the bloody bottle of shampoo again, and squirt into my palm the equivalent of what I've lost in my earlier attempt to knock myself out. Holding my left hand in my right hand, I finally connect with my hair and rub in the shampoo. Some of it goes into my other eye, but I'm on the last lap now and I no longer care about the pain. I don't know how long it might be before I can do this again, so I rub and rub and rub until there's a lather like Father Christmas's beard.

I lunge forward with my head, stopping this time just before the water pipe. I feel the shampoo rinsing out of my hair. After a long, long time I pull my head back, and rest it on the back wall. Water drips on to the white ceramic of the cistern.

I pick up the towel, wrap it round my head and do an appalling job of drying my hair. I don't really care. I can turn to look at myself in the mirror without having to stand up. I finally manage to connect with the comb, with my right hand. I can't hold it between a finger and thumb, but must wrap my whole hand round it. I try to comb my hair. Neither of my hands will obey me, and I'm spending as much time combing the bare skin of my forehead as I am touching any hair. My hand keeps swooping and swirling, like a swallow diving down from a roof. I give up on a proper parting, and stop when most of my hair is at least reasonably straight, glued to my scalp by the water.

Have I the energy to get back home? To my bed, I mean. I retrieve my gown from the basin, and finally get both arms through the holes. The gown is wet, filthy. It stinks.

Laboriously, I go through the routine of putting on the belt, the gown and the sponge bag. I hate putting the soiled gown back on again on my now cleaner flesh. It feels tacky, soiled.

I don't know what my body is doing, but it must be producing something that is putting me on a high. I feel elated. Or is it just that I feel cleansed? I'm able to concentrate hard and negotiate the tricky business of opening a door with a Zimmer frame in front of me. It was easy coming in, I just kicked out behind me to knock the door shut.

I'm finding it best to take each step as a separate entity and move myself forward by thinking, not about the journey but just about one step at a time. Just like an alcoholic: I will not have a drink *today*. I find I'm waiting ten, twenty or even thirty seconds between each step. Extraordinary that no one has stopped to challenge me. I think I'm walking quite well. Later, as I go on interminable Zimmer runs with my wife standing by me, she tells me I'm leaning like the Tower of Pisa, 'walking' in spasmodic shuffles rather than steps. I'm oblivious to this. I think I'm doing rather well, except that great waves of tiredness are sweeping over me, and at times, I just have to stop completely and close my eyes.

Only once does disaster loom. Without warning, the left leg of the Zimmer frame sticks and catches on the floor. I'm committed to moving forward, and I seem to collide with the frame. I struggle frantically to stay upright, pull myself back in a desperate attempt not to fall forward over the frame, but succeed instead in pulling the whole frame completely off the floor. It waves around. It is incredibly light, and for a moment, I wish it weighed a ton, was rooted to the floor and I could root myself to it. For a long moment I seem to be hanging in mid-air, then the frame grounds and I am back on earth.

At last, at very, very long last, I'm standing by my bed. I swing the Zimmer frame round, and plonk down on the mattress. My head bangs on the TV screen that I've not swung back far enough. Great. At this rate I'll need a crash helmet. So far today I've bashed my head, my knuckles and my gums.

It has taken me well over an hour to go a few yards to the bathroom, shave (sort of), wash my hair (sort of) and come back.

And no one seems to have noticed that I've been gone.

Theoretically, I should be bed-bound. Later, I find the explanation. It's now Saturday. The weekend shift has come on. I think it's actually a double shift, days and nights. Who owns this ward? Who takes final responsibility for it? Or like the Presidency of the EU, does it shift all the time? I presume the new shift has been told about the state of the patients. Whatever they've been told, it has not been enough to register that for forty-five minutes or so the patient in Bed 4 wasn't there. I'd disobeyed orders, sadly not for the first time in my life.

The stale smell of my gown is irritating. My son went out yesterday to buy a new pair of pyjamas, and they're in my locker, unwrapped from their Marks & Spencer packaging. This is the last hurdle. I lean forward, grab the trousers wildly. Sitting on the edge of the bed, I hang on to them with my right hand while my right leg tries to find the right hole. Success! No! The right leg has gone in to the left leg.

I feel like crying. Another of those mood swings. I fight it. I yank my leg out, try again. It's like one of those infuriating puzzles you buy in shops, where round and square objects surrounded by an oily, clear liquid have to be floated into their respective round and square holes. Bloody hell! This is my own sodding leg, and I can't even put it into the correct leg on a pair of pyjama trousers. Inside my head, the language is getting worse by the minute.

From somewhere, a deep, bubbling laugh is given birth inside me at around stomach level, and rising.

I'm fifty-six years old, and a Terribly (Self) Important Man With A Good Job. And all the rest of it. But today, actually, I'm someone feeling very, very small, and very, very frightened, who can't even put his bloody right leg into a pair of pyjama trousers.

And it is very, very funny. Ludicrous. Absurd. Beyond belief. Bring on the clowns. All the pomposity, the absurdity of pretension, the years of experience in the final count come to one thing. Telling your leg to go where you, rather than it, want it to go.

And I, who have spent so much of my life telling other people what to do, am finally reduced to a fearsome, to-the-death conflict with...

My own leg.

It is suddenly very, very funny, and it sure does put a lot of other conflicts in perspective.

The Diary of a Stroke

I start to shake with laughter. Uncontrollable, glorious laughter at the sheer absurdity of the whole thing.

Revelation 1 on the road to recovery. The memory of my long-dead father's words of wisdom, that stroke victims have a launch window (my words, not his) of time within which they decide if they are victims or victors.

Revelation 2 on the road to recovery. Regaining a sense of humour, the capacity to laugh out the mood swings that threatened recovery.

I've yet to learn the further routes. But these are enough for now.

I've done quite a bit of reading about strokes since I had mine, perhaps to make up for lost time. But there are some things you don't find in medical or quasi-medical books. Like the fact that my right leg doesn't like being laughed at. After all these years of being under my command so totally that I did not even realise I was issuing orders, a mutinous blood clot has gone on the rampage and cut all communication with Headquarters.

This is my right leg's chance of a break for freedom. Fifty-four or -five years of being forced to go ... forward. No vote on it. No choice for the leg. No democracy here. No chance to express an opinion.

What if going ... backwards would have allowed my leg to get back in touch with its ... *backwards* side? Or its inner leg? What if it just didn't want to move, because it had fallen out with its dear partner, my left leg? Man the barricades. That lonely, brave blood clot has brought the whole Fascist, totalitarian state machinery of my body to a grinding halt, destroying itself in the process like a suicide bomber. It is Iraq after the fall of Sadaam Hussein. Now is my right leg's chance! Revolution! Particularly as my left leg is in a drunken stupor, unable to do anything of its own volition.

I'm shaking with laughter. The image in my mind is of my rebellious right leg, marching on its own with a placard screaming 'THE RIGHT LEG DEMANDS FREEDOM' stuck between its toes (providing they hadn't joined a different rebellion). And rather ignoring the fact that a leg on its own has no meaning, no reason for existence. A leg is there to serve. It's part of a greater thing, the body, which in turn is there only to support an even greater thing, the mind. And the mind...

Well, never mind that just now.

I find myself talking to my leg.

Reader, this isn't something I've done before.

I hope I'm doing it silently, though I'm so convulsed with laughter, I can't be sure.

I understand your desire for freedom, I find myself saying to my own leg. But the plain truth of it is, when legs become disconnected from the body, they don't march to a glorious future. They go to the incinerator. In a nasty, stained brown parcel. I know this, because I worked for two summer vacations as a hospital porter at the old Sheffield Royal Infirmary (where, by the way, no dirt lived on a ward for longer than a second, and the nurses were too terrified of Matron to talk to their own mothers, never mind each other). In that job I sometimes had to carry the severed limbs away from the operating theatres.

Now, I'll excuse you this once, leg. You've clearly been carried away by the rather unusual prevailing circumstances. Now come back, please. Normal service must be resumed as soon as possible. Pyjamas, right leg. Occupant, my right leg. NOW STOP FARTING AROUND AND GET IN THERE!'

And it does. Certainly reluctantly, perhaps even mutinously. But it does.

Left leg is asleep, so I just use my good arm to bundle it in. I'm undoubtedly losing it: I'm treating each individual limb as if it were a person. Where will this end? Am I going to have heart to hearts with my toes? Suddenly, I've new, clean, fresh-smelling pyjama trousers on. It's the best smell in the world. I'm decent. And clean.

Now I can take off the hated surgical gown, drop it to the floor without being indecent. I take a cheerful three minutes to undo the top button on the pyjama top. Getting it on is a joke. My arms will not raise up above my shoulders, however much I concentrate and try to make them do it. I have to hold the top open in front of me at chest height, and lunge forward with my head, aiming at the hole. It works.

The male nurse walks in. He's a card. He knows he's a card. He flirts shamelessly with the women, and could be gay. Hello, he says, feeling better, are you?

I sense it would not be good news to tell him that in the last three quarters of an hour, I could have broken my hip, knocked myself unconscious, bashed my head in on a shower pipe, broken a lavatory pan by sitting down on it too hard (the injuries from that don't bear thinking about) and flooded the hospital. Instead I try to smile (I still have very limited control over my facial muscles) and ask if my sheets can be changed.

Recuperation

I can hear the slurring in my speech, and two or three times I nearly out-pace the words, my thoughts working faster than my brain can turn them into spoken words.

The nurse's expression darkens slightly. 'Soon', he says, after a moment's thought. Sheets aren't his thing. Suddenly, I want the sheets changed more than anything else. They're the thin, crumpled things you get in hospital, and they're dirty. My dirt. The dirt that has come off my body. The dirt I've just washed off me. Those sheets are yesterday, and I want today to start now.

A very fat girl in some sort of uniform comes in and asks what I want for breakfast. A number of the staff are very overweight, and from the smell some of them seem to be heavy smokers. Physician, heal thyself. She looks very unhappy, and never allows her eyes to meet mine, or even rise much above floor level. I ask for muesli, yogurt and tea. Then I realise that my wife will be coming, with at least one of my sons, and they might be hungry. I add toast on to the order, and feel a sense of guilt that I'm stretching the NHS budget.

In the middle of all this, Mr Frankland, in the next door bed, suddenly lets off a fart that would have done justice to a D-Day bombardment. It is raucous, loud and incredibly long. It seems to go on for minutes, falling to a level that leads me to think it must at last be coming to an end before rising up a tone and continuing with renewed vigour. Everyone seems oblivious. The girl collecting breakfast orders does not even flinch. Mr Frankland lies there, apparently disowning any ownership. Right at the end, the male orderly comes in.

'Did that one have lumps in it, Harry?' he asks cheerfully. He does not wait for an answer – Harry can speak quite coherently, but often reduces himself to saying, 'Ho, hah. Ho hah…' several times over at conversational volume levels.

The male nurse goes over to the other side of the ward, to the bed containing the semi-comatose old man. He talks to him, loudly, cheerfully. He lifts the sheets off the old man, surprisingly gently. He's about to give him a bed bath, and also manipulate him so he does not get bed sores or deep-vein thrombosis. I only see the preliminaries. Very quickly the curtains are drawn round the bed. What happens now I find so interesting. The loud, swaggering nurse – is he so like a cock in a hen run because he's the only male nurse among so many women? – becomes soft and gentle with the old man, expert, surprisingly delicate in his handling of the dead lump and sagging flesh of a body. He keeps up a conversation with the old man, who can only grunt occasionally in reply, but the conversation is also different from the *braggadocio* crap he churns out in public. It is almost respectful, cajoling. Whatever is happening to that old man behind the curtains, it isn't destroying his dignity.

To spoil the mood, as the curtains are being drawn, the old man lets out a loud belch. Illness comes down to this, in the end. Fluids and wetness, wind and stench, all the awfulness of decay.

The behaviour of the male nurse is touching. Had I glanced at the clock, and had a little knowledge, I would have been less reassured. Why? Time is of the essence, as contracts say, but they're not usually matters of life or death, or of living death.

The crucial first hours

Most of the damage done by a stroke takes place in the first six hours. I've spent the first of those arguing stupidly with various people that I don't need to go to hospital, and the last lying in a darkened ward feeling myself degrade, with virtually no medical attention paid to me whatsoever.

It is difficult, even now, not to feel extreme anger at what wasn't done, counterbalanced only by my eternal gratitude to the ambulance man. He could only take me to hospital with my consent, did not have patience with the patient from Hell and talked me into saying yes. I am also grateful to my friend who stayed with me for the rest of that night.

Why the anger? My stroke (or 'cerebrovascular accident') is caused by a blockage or clot in one of the arteries that supplies blood to the brain. This is (probably) caused by 'atrial fibrillation', or an irregular or weak heartbeat; this leaves blood in the relatively large cavities of the heart and so can allow clots to form. Moving blood is healthy blood. Static blood solidifies. Fibrillation means the blood isn't pumped out of the heart properly. It hangs around rather too long. A clot forms. The heart goes back to a normal rhythm, and shoots the clot out into the blood stream, where it sticks at some point in the narrow avenues of my circulation system.

The fact of what's happening to me could have been established very rapidly. My medical history screams it at any questioner. Over 50. Male (more men than women under 70 have strokes). Overweight. History of atrial fibrillation. History of hypertension (high blood pressure).

Next question. Is this a 'transient ischaemic attack (TIA)', or a mini-stroke? TIA's are, basically, blockages which pass through or dissipate quickly. Symptoms rarely last more than 24 hours; without treatment, 30% of sufferers who undergo a TIA are likely to have a major stroke within three years.

This isn't a TIA, as could have been established early on. There are seventeen physical and mental symptoms of a full-blown stroke. I tick 13 boxes, to me, at least, an extraordinarily high figure:

- paralysis or weakness of the muscles
- involuntary jerking movements
- loss of sensation on one side of the body
- complete lack of feeling on the left-hand side of my face
- difficulty in swallowing
- slurred speech
- sight problems
- loss of 'righting reflexes' – balance, posture and movement
- general tiredness and lack of stamina
- confusion
- memory loss
- loss of concentration and organisational skills
- psychological problems: anxiety, frustration, depression and anger.

Most of these could have been explained by another

illness, of course. Candidates include Alzheimer's Disease, a brain tumour, multiple sclerosis, epilepsy or head injury.

But no one asks me, during those first crucial hours in hospital. No one gives me anything approaching an intensive questioning, either about my medical history or my symptoms. Instead, I'm bundled on to a trolley, and then a bed. And I push my feet against someone's hand. The someone is a doctor, basically a girl with a lot of factual knowledge, no bedside manner and a busy-busy demeanour that suggests not so much that I am in pain, but that I am rather a pain for being ill.

The questions should have led them to what type of stroke I'd had. I did not lose consciousness. 60% of strokes occur when the patient is awake. Loss of consciousness generally occurs when the patient has had a haemorrhage, or bleeding into the brain. The reason why it is so important to establish the type of stroke is that it determines the treatment the patient should get.

I've a very vivid memory of undergoing an MRI scan (Magnetic Resonance Imaging). It's a long, noisy and rather frighteningly claustrophobic experience. It's crucial in identifying a haemorrhage, a tumour or damaged tissue, and thus making clear what has actually happened to the patient. It's a vital and expensive diagnostic test. My problem is that I've no memory of it happening while I was in the hospital to which I allowed myself to be admitted when I had my stroke. It takes place quite a few weeks afterwards, when I'm under the care of a quite ferocious consultant. That I do remember. I do remember in-hospital blood tests, a chest X-ray and a CT scan. This latter is the poor man's MRI. It slices the brain up into

X-rays and reveals haemorrhage and tumour, but not the early incidence of dead tissue. At the time, I'm aware of a tremendous lack of urgency about all these procedures. It is as if I'm simply the next on the list. The sub-text is very clear. I'm going to be ill for a very long time. There's no hurry to prove this.

The most worrying thing, among very many things that I'm not told, is that the brain reacts like a computer does to unused icons on Microsoft. If you don't use it, the brain tends to switch it off. The left-hand side of my face isn't working, my hands aren't working, my legs aren't working properly. And I'm desperate for them to. My anger to get them going results in my firing increasingly intense signals to my brain to wake them up. The control circuits are hardly responding, if at all, to my conscious mind. At some deeper level, I'm sending the neurones in my brain a continuous wake-up call. I can't say how much I would have given at the time for someone to tell me that just sending the signals was all-important, and that the reply could come later. As it is, I feel like someone marooned in space. My favourite film is *Alien*. In hospital, no one hears you scream.

The day continues.

I'm excited as I wait for my wife, counting down the minutes. She will have to get up, wash, have breakfast and then find her way out to the hospital, some way out of the part of the city where she's staying with my son. She must be exhausted. She will ask no sympathy from anyone. She never does. She just gets on with it and copes. She will have to drive herself through a strange city in rush hour, in all probability to stick a cheerful face on at the sight of the physical, and possibly mental, wreck the man she married has become.

I decided over thirty years ago that illness is actually harder for those who have to visit than it is for those who have the illness. People help the patient. The patient can, at least, try to help himself. The relative or friend can only sit, watch and try to offer support, with precious few support mechanisms for them.

I try not to work out the time too closely. What's the earliest she can be with me? At the back of my mind, there's real fear for her. She has stood by me through cancer, is in a new and demanding job, has moved house and home to a city where we know virtually no one. I can sense an obsessive selfishness growing in me – or perhaps it has been there all along and the stroke has simply released it. How much pressure can my wife, and my family, stand? Yet I'm excited, because, although I know all sorts of things are still terribly wrong, including my eyesight, my frightening lack of control over my arms and hands, my terrible struggling to walk even with a Zimmer frame, and my chronic vision, I've actually improved. Here, perhaps, I'm very lucky not to know too much.

Dead brain cells swell with fluid, placing more pressure on the system, but the fluid is absorbed fairly rapidly, the swelling decreases and there's often a sharp improvement. It can be deceptive. Some months later, I'm reading a book about strokes. It is a rather good book in many respects. It states:

'At first the outlook can seem bleak. However, while pessimism may be understandable, it isn't justified in the vast majority of cases. Though full recovery from a stroke is rare, most stroke patients regain a reasonable degree of independence.'

A reasonable degree of independence. Reasonable as defined by who?

Though I deeply regret the many things that aren't told me and which I don't know, I don't regret at all being spared this piece of information. I don't know that a full recovery is rare. Therefore, I'm assuming that I can make a full recovery and am determined to do so. It is slowly becoming my target. It's what you do, isn't it? You fall ill. You get better.

Breakfast arrives. I've ordered muesli. I spill most of it on to the towel I've draped over the bed. My hand simply will not hold the spoon properly, can't direct it to my mouth. The tea is a joke. I don't even try to drink it; I can't even close forefinger and thumb round the cup handle.

My wife appears in the doorway. I'm sitting up in bed, pretending to read a newspaper bought from the brilliant volunteer lady who has wheeled a goody trolley round. I can't actually focus on the print for half the time, but I'm fooling myself I can do it for far longer. I'm in clean pyjamas, my hair is washed and combed, and if my face bears an uncomfortable resemblance to set-aside, at least someone has taken some care over the crop. I grin at my wife. It is slightly lop-sided, but it is still a grin.

She must sense something different in me. Now, all these months on, I wonder what she was expecting to see? In any event, what she sees now is very different from what she left the night before. I wish I could bottle or preserve the expression in her eyes and on her face.

Recuperation

I get a distinct lift from the sense of her sudden surge of hope.

The problem is that I've used up all my energy in the crawl to the bathroom. I'm excited, but exhausted.

The day rolls on. My blood pressure is taken regularly, and something stuck in my ear to measure my temperature. Medicine seems very dependent on orifices. Blood pressure and temperature are fine. My wife reads, looks up at me regularly and fires off a question or a comment. My employers have now been told about my illness in full. They're supportive, positive to my wife. They could not be better. For almost the first time in my life, I'm not thinking about work. It isn't because I don't care. It is because I need my illness to talk to me, tell me if this is permanent, before I can let myself think about work.

I'm occasionally looked at, in a vague sort of way. But there's an absence of what I would call nursing. I'm there, and I've got to be fed and measured at regular intervals. As a person with thoughts and feelings, I'm not there. The nursing staff have a faraway look in their eyes, as if they're thinking about anything except the patient. Only the male nurse introduces himself to me by name. There seems to be no one in charge of the ward, no central spine to its authority.

The ward is also dirty. I have seen no one clean it since I arrived. There are those containers of alcohol-like hand rub everywhere, telling you to keep your hands clean all the time, but there's still a pile of dust and fluff under my bedside cabinet, and under the bed.

Lunch arrives. There's soup, which I can't eat because I can't hold any hot fluid safely. There's something that claims to be Shepherd's Pie. Someone might have waved a tin of meat in front of the watery mash, but clearly they took it away very quickly before running the risk of opening it. My wife looks with deep suspicion at the plate and the tinned fruit dumped into a bowl. The menu is brought for supper. It consists of sandwiches. It is raining hard now. My wife announces she's going out to buy some decent food from somewhere. By now I'm very tired. So, I suspect, is she.

I doze, fall asleep. I don't know what time it is when my wife returns, but it's getting dark. Her hair is wet, and there's water on her face and soaked through her sodden coat. I find out much later the water on her face is tears, not rainwater. She has found a small Marks & Spencer's, bought me a salmon salad and sat down for a cup of tea. Then she has cried, despair at what the future holds for us breaking through her iron control very briefly. You wouldn't know it from the way she talks to me, cheerfully, never showing any doubt, any of the terrible fears that must plague her.

It is dark now outside, and other people are visiting. There's no one for Mr Frankland, who has asked to borrow my paper but has left it on his lap as he stares out of the window vacantly. Suddenly he lies down, and turns over. He goes to sleep as visitors start to pile in. In the far corner the old man's son and his young wife come to visit. The son talks cheerfully to the father, and spends much time sorting out the TV. He relaxes visibly when they find some soccer on a channel. He spends much time asking his father if he would like to watch the soccer, and with an almost audible sigh sits back to do so himself. The wife wanders off somewhere. The other old man, opposite me, also has a visit from his wife. She's a small, sparrow-like creature with white hair and bright, tired eyes. She talks gently to him for long periods, then falls silent. He hardly answers at all, never looking at her.

My middle son is on the duty watch, and he has brought a rocket salad. The hospital supper is dire, white-bread sandwiches with processed filling. My wife, who was going to do her PhD on some aspect of chemistry related to the food industry, works out the nutritional value of the meal. It is nil. My wife and son hang up a small tent around me again, to catch flying food. My hands have the shakes, and they've seen what happens when I try to feed myself. I manage to do three extraordinarily difficult things – spear a bit of salmon on a fork, bring it to my mouth and ram it in. My middle son grins, sticks a large leaf of rocket on his forehead and asks, 'Who am I?' We all laugh, genuinely. This ward is appearing more like a mausoleum as each hour goes by, and laughter keeps the darkness at bay.

I announce I'm going for a Zimmer. It is even harder than it was this morning, which now seems days away. The surging effect is so strong that when I hold on to the Zimmer frame, I actually lift it up off the floor on the up-surge. I'm having great trouble co-ordinating the frame and my legs. The frame seems to be getting beyond them for some reason, leaving my legs outside the protection of its three-sided square. I bash my leg, the left one of course, into the frame, topple and start to fall. My wife catches me and, for a moment, she has to bear nearly all my weight. We hang there, poised. I recover. I shout at her, criticising her for helping me. I have to do it on my own. I'm ashamed of my rudeness. We make it just beyond the bathroom, but far more slowly than this morning. Turning round is hell. I manage it, just.

We keep on doing this. Again and again. It is my introduction to the mindless, sapping routines that will dominate my life for weeks to come. We plan each trip. We're going to the door of the ward. We're going to the bathroom, to the nurses' station. It seems to go on forever, and, sometimes, I seem to be regressing.

I'm tired, my wife is tired and my son has a partner to go back to having just given up his Saturday. I plead with them to leave. We've nothing more to say to each other. My wife is exhausted, though I defy any outsider to see it. I am so proud of her. I'm pleased for her when she finally agrees to go, and then worry about her falling asleep on the way home to my son's house and driving off the road.

I get up just once more, and use the Zimmer frame to take three steps. It is still not good, but it is definitely better than it was when I was with my wife. Now I feel I've earned a DVD. My middle son has set up the laptop on the bed table, loaded the DVD. All I have to do is hold one hand with the other and hit the button. He knows my taste. *Star Wars*. I manage about half of it before I fall asleep.

Day 4

Sunday morning. I'm awake at 6.30am again. When I was in private care for my cancer surgery, they brought a cup of tea first thing in the morning. It was a simple thing, but it made a difference. Not that I would have been able to drink it, without my rebel hand splurging it around the ward.

I should by now have met a physiotherapist – a rather nice girl had dropped by on Friday, I think, and told me that she was off for the weekend but would pop in on Monday. She informed me I would have to do lots of exercises, not mentioning what they were, and also that I should meet a speech therapist and various other specialists. Like the cup of tea, it would have been nice. Unlike the cup of tea, I could also have used it.

I want to know prognosis, diagnosis, and whether I've a career any more or not. There's absolutely no sense of urgency in this ward, no drive, no energy. It is as if there's a complete split between what the doctors do on their rare visits – I'll see a doctor visit the three old men in the ward only once during my stay there – and what the nurses do. The nurses aren't part of the medical programme. Their job isn't to mend the body or even to heal the mind. It is to keep the body pretty much where it was when they first met it. They do it perfectly decently. Sometimes they show real kindness. But they're onlookers, somehow not involved in the healing process, but observing it.

I'm reminded of taking my dog into kennels. The kennels' job isn't to train my dog, cure my dog if it is ill, or love it and nurture it. Their job is to return my dog to me in more or less the same shape as it was when I handed it in. They'll treat it professionally, cater for its basic needs. It'll be fed, and when that process reaches its natural end, it'll be cleaned up after. The kennel assistant, a gorgeous girl who loves animals, will do what my dog needs doing to it, speak nicely to it, maybe even stroke it. But all the time she will be thinking if she can make it to the cinema that night to meet her boyfriend, whether she has saved enough to buy an old car. She's semi-detached. My nurses are semi-detached. I cringe internally as I write this. They're nice people. That's why they've come in to nursing. But someone should tell them the difference between nursing and just being there.

Or is it because some of them quite like the power? I'm trying not to think of Harold Shipman.

But do I really wish someone had told me the facts? Is part of getting better never conceding that one won't? I remember a man I once knew who had broken his neck playing rugby. He had an iron determination to walk and move again. Once a fortnight or so he summoned up the strength to stand up, with assistance. He never made it any further. That one motion of standing up for a few seconds cost him his whole personality. Never a nice man, I suspect, he became a single-minded, focused, driving personality, someone who seemed to live for, rather than despite, his disability. Will I be like that? I shudder and dismiss the thought. I've never been good at dismissing thoughts, but I'm learning fast.

I swing my legs out of the bed. Is the sea slightly less rough this morning, or is it my imagination? I stand up, using the Zimmer frame. This morning I've set myself another bathroom challenge. I'm going to take a shower. But I frightened myself a bit yesterday, and I want to check that I can stand up. What is incredible is that no one has commented on what I did yesterday. Nobody has asked me how I washed myself, or even if I wanted washing. None of the nurses have noticed. I'm effectively on my own in this ward and this hospital. It's me versus the stroke.

The system works. Sponge bag dropped down front, resting on pyjama trouser tie cord this time, the pyjama jacket tucked into the trousers. Towel. Slippers.

We're off. Vroom vroom vroom. Except it's more like chug, clunk, clang, a wonky old engine firing on three cylinders, veering from one side of the road to the other.

Now I've got some confidence back, I'm over-optimistic both about how fast I can go and how straight I can steer. I frighten myself by nearly falling over on a number of occasions, on one of them being saved only by having the wall stop my fall.

I position the Zimmer frame by the shower, open the door with one hand. Back kick to shut it. Why waste energy turning round? I have to step up into the well at the bottom of the shower. One small step for mankind. Bloody terrifying for me. Oh well. Here goes. Very carefully, one hand still on the Zimmer, I place my left foot inside the shower. Now the big moment. I move the right one as well, timing it with the waves that are still heaving me up and down. I put my hand out, grip the water pipe that leads up the shower head. It's OK. I'm standing up. Having proved the point, I lean on the wall for support.

I turn on the shower.

The cold water hits me, and I gasp with the shock. I fumble with the temperature controls, worrying that I'll move from freezing cold to scalding my whole body. The water turns from cold to tepid. I leave it at that. Feeling that water sluicing off me is the best feeling I've had since the illness, better even than washing my hair. I stand and stand and stand, head raised up, feeling the water bounce off my eyelids, leaning on the wall, swaying. Or is the swaying simply in my head, my body actually still? I risk the temperature control, turn up the heat. I'm not really in control of my hands, but I work out how to do an emergency cold if by accident I push the water up to boiling. There's steam in the room now, and the mirror mists over. This is a real shower. It's brilliant.

As I climb out of the shower, I either have my hand on the now-hot pipe, or the Zimmer. The first one burns. There must have been a brief, flickering moment when my hand was on neither. I don't remember it.

The shave this morning is slightly less like Sweeney Todd when he's drunk, though complicated by the fact that uncontrollable fits of the shivers are passing through my body. It's still very disarming to find the hand holding the razor going walkabout with no advance warning, swooping down, ending up with the razor resting on my shoulder blade. No damage done, but I'd better start buying shares in whoever makes styptic pencils. If anyone does make them any more.

I'm over-confident getting back to the ward, and bang into an oxygen cylinder. The cylinder wobbles, but doesn't fall over. I wobble, but don't fall over. Disaster averted. But still the whole world is wobbling, like the Weeble toys my boys had when they were little.

I haven't put slippers on for this visit. The tension and the excitement made me forget. I've just had a shower, so the soles of my feet were clean at the point of departure. Back home to my bed. And I've walked back, with bare soles, for what is in any real terms a very short distance, through half a normal size ward in an NHS hospital.

It is an NHS increasingly fixated on MRSA, the killer illness that we have let in to our hospitals through failure to keep them clean. I have not seen a cleaner since I was admitted. As a student, doing that vacation job as a hospital porter in the summer at the old Sheffield Royal Infirmary, I was turned away from the door of a ward because Matron said I had dirty shoes. I'm too relieved to be back in bed to realise the significance of this, but a distant part of my brain (perhaps the same part that made me forget to put my slippers on) remembers slide marks. Big, black slide marks from dirt on the soles of my feet, as I slide them down the luxury of the clean white sheets. I feel a sense of guilt, like a naughty schoolboy. Someone will notice the mess I've made and tell me off.

Matron will disapprove.

In fact, nobody notices. Nobody tells me off. Why would anybody in this ward concern themselves with black marks on sheets?

And anyway, what do I care? I've no wound for the infection to get into, not a physical one, anyway. And I've walked a few pathetic steps.

Then comes the bad news.

I write a lot, use a computer to communicate via email far too much. I'm a professional. When it's really important I hand-write letters to people. When I write my books, the private part of me that's so important to my self-respect, I work on a keyboard. My first book was written on a manual typewriter. I'm old enough to have written my first book on a *manual* typewriter. Then, it was a golf-ball electronic typewriter (state of the art: it rarely worked), and then, an early Amstrad computer with a green screen – green as in colour, not eco-friendliness. I knew the Dark Ages of Technology, and I've walked through them. And now I have got a laptop.

My laptop is by the bed, still where my son set it up last night. On a whim, I take it out. To my surprise, I have to try three times to hit the 'On' button. Finally, I switch it on.

I try to type out,

'I'm going to type again on a keyboard.'

What appears on the screen is,

]IAMQ foi,nhj rto eetpe Aago'm;

How bad is this? There's a pen in the computer case, and a pad of paper. The pen feels like a leaden weight in my hand as soon as I hold it in writing position, like the razor. It's a snake that at any moment is going to

74

turn round and bite my hand. It's chopsticks that weigh several tons. I can't actually get my head into a writing position. However I rest it, the muscles feel locked. I try to sign my name, the simple thing I've done at least a million million times throughout my life.

The result is an indecipherable squiggle of meaningless lines and gross loops.

You're having to learn to walk again, which you did at the age of two, and now you're going to have to try and learn to write again, which you did at the age of five. Have to? The issue is: can it be done? I'm desperate for decent advice. The writing and the keyboard skills aren't just crucial to my professional life. They're crucial to my whole sense of who I am.

For thirty years now I've been writing books, ranging from little booklets to academic works, nineteen of them in total. Now I'm writing novels, historical crime thrillers, and the edited manuscript of my fourth is about to land on the doorstep, for me to make detailed comments on the editing and, no doubt, rewrite chunks of it. My editor is totally piranha-like in seeking out rubbish in what I write. How will I cope if I can't hit a keyboard? Will I have to dictate my next novel to a secretary, and pay them for it? Henry James dictated his later novels. Maybe this is why I can't stand reading Henry James.

The fear that I may have lost the physical capacity to write sticks with me. I like to top and tail the letters I send from work, writing in old-fashioned fountain pen the 'Dear...' and the 'Yours sincerely...' If I can't do this any more, will I in effect be hanging a large sign on my door saying, 'DISABLED'? I'm starting to see the world through the eyes of those who are disabled, after the experience with the taps in the shower room, and now this. It is a very different view.

The fear of not writing is like a permanent toothache. Over and above that, I begin to realise the dreadful monotony of life on the ward. All the stimuli are negative. The three old men are asleep, even though the light is streaming in through the smeared windows. In a single room one has the benefit of silence, space to contemplate. In one of the old, long wards I imagine the loss of privacy was in part compensated for by the interest of seeing what was going on in the whole ward, feeling part of its bustle and life.

Here in a ward with four beds there's neither silence nor privacy. It's the worst of both worlds. For most of the time one is on public display. If, and when, the curtains are drawn, there's an illusion of visual privacy, but no privacy of sound. When they draw the curtains on the old man across left to give him a bed bath, the sucking, wet noises from inside the plastic tent conjure up visual pictures that are probably far uglier than the reality of what's happening. I'm not a part of a main ward, merely stuck in a side room shared with three other near-corpses, but all the noise that is the outside ward bustles in through the ever-open door. The result is a strange mixture. Life, in the form of well people and professionals, flows round the four patients like a stream flows round rocks. Flows round. Does not engage. Who wants to talk to a rock? Is it my imagination, or have there been four sets of care teams working in the ward since I was admitted? Weekday day and night staff, weekend day and night staff. Yet some seem to have stayed the same. I would have been quite interested to know the system they're working, but I feel unable to ask. I'm a body in the ward, not a body with a brain.

I buy a paper, the *Sunday Times*. My eyes can focus a bit better now. It's not perfect, not even good, but I can read a few sentences before the pain comes back. My football team has lost again, the journalists are creating stories where they can't actually find one and the paper is filled with a sense of outrage at everything except newspapers and journalists. No change there, then. Mr Frankland next door is awake now. He asks if he can borrow my paper, and again takes it to his bed, but does not read it.

A thought hits me. Was it the Fat Consultant who told me? Or my wife? Or did I just know it anyway? Wherever. I know that a leg recovers faster than an arm. Damn.

I tell my wife about my writing. She goes out and buys a thick, lined A4 pad. If I can start trying to write now, and if over a few days we can see it getting better, maybe it will spur me on. I decide I will write out the alphabet, one line to each letter, repeating the letters for as long as there is space on the line. Then I will fill some more lines with my signature. Surely that should be easier to write than anything else, given the number of times – billions? – I've written it in my life? I pick up a pen, a cheap blue biro with a chewed end, and try to write my signature. The pen skids all over the paper. I seem to have almost no control of it at all. I try to write 'a a a a...' The resulting squiggle is horrific, anarchic. The letters blur, and I'm having trouble seeing. It's because there are tears welling up in my eyes.

I stop writing, start up again only when I get home. It is just too much for me at the moment. I will learn to write again. But not now.

My wife is worried about the old man opposite. An orderly brings his flaccid lunch, cardboard and processed plastic, but he does not eat it. We ask the orderly if anyone can help him to eat.

'Not my job,' says the orderly, 'I'm not allowed to help a patient to eat. I can only bring the food.'

We tell a nurse, and she nods and smiles. 'Do you want your food, Harry?' she says. He grunts. 'I'll leave it there for you,' she says, and goes.

My wife asks the nurse if she can feed Harry herself. 'No, of course not,' she says. 'You're not qualified.' She may not be qualified. But she is more than capable of helping an old man to eat, which is more than any of the paid staff seem willing to do.

The other old man, far left, keeps the TV on continually, loudly, on a sport channel. He does not appear to be looking at it. It is strangely unsettling, like being in the video store and hearing the soundtrack of a film without being able to see it.

Today is Zimmer day. I'm going to become an expert Zimmer-racer, and am determined to impress my wife with my motoring skills. The progress since yesterday is noticeable. It's the turning that's the problem, and the co-ordination between the arms and the legs. Speed is still dreadfully slow.

When I was in for cancer, sore-looking men would be

marching up and down the corridors with grim-faced determination, following strong hints from the nursing staff that it was good to get up and about. I'm alone on the ward corridor, where the nurses seem to gather behind the nurses' station as if it were a protective barricade. The nurse who I think is in charge is thin and ferocious. She never smiles, and looks all the time as if someone had just told her she's about to get paid less.

I'm starting to worry about work now. People are being kind, but the sense of powerlessness is almost overwhelming at times. I'm worried about my wife's work as well. She's not complaining, but I can see how tired she is. Illness is easier on the patient than it is on those who love them. The patient is fussed over, the centre of attention. The others simply have to wait, suffer and watch.

As a final fling my wife has the idea she could walk me to the ward's dayroom. It has a big TV. It might be easier to watch that than the bedside set. I want to walk, at least for a few paces, but decide I'll have to be sneaky. I'm still not good, even with the Zimmer. My wife hovers by me as I Zimmer, a worried look on her face. She has enough to be worried about. Thank God she didn't see me and the razor that first time. We arrive in the dayroom in record time. I feel encouraged.

I'll walk unaided for the first time in the evening, when she's gone.

The dayroom is hospital grey, has tattered books in it and the large TV. It's empty. Patients don't use the dayroom on The Ward Of The Dead. There's a dash of colour, though: cards litter the surfaces and the window ledge. Wonderful, I think. I pick one up.

'Thank you,' it says, 'for making Henry's last few hours on Earth so peaceful...'

Many cards seem to be thanking the staff for being good to someone who has died.

I must, I say to my wife, get out of this place. Soon.

They won't let you, she says, glumly. I grip the Zimmer frame even more fiercely, and in my imagination there's a steely glint in my eyes. Even though they're still rolling in opposite directions. Surely you can have a steely glint *and* roll in opposite directions. I am forced to admit that eyes looking in two directions at the same time does wonders for reducing the authority of anything you say. Would any of my pupils take me seriously if I bollocked them with my eyes swivelling left and right? No need to answer that.

The dayroom is by the door that leads to the outside world. It is the door to Heaven. I look at the door, and yearn. Leaving Heaven aside for the minute, that door to the outside is also the wardrobe door that leads to Narnia. Except I don't want to escape to a fantasy world. My ideal Narnia would operate in reverse. I want to get back to the real world. I want to be out of this place. It is becoming like a prison.

After my wife and son leave, I try to read a book. The words keep blurring, and my head hurts. I look hard at the light over the ward door. There are still two of them, but they coalesce into one if I try very hard for longer than two or three minutes. My headache gets worse.

It's nine o'clock. I swing my legs out of the bed. The floor feels cold. I noticed this morning how filthy the soles of my feet had become. Do I wear slippers for this first walk, or do I need to have the close contact of bare feet on the floor? Wake up, son. If you're going to walk to work, you won't be doing it barefoot. And it spares the sheets.

I put on the slippers, stand up. Heavy swell, not gale force. Not yet. I look longingly at the Zimmer frame. I push it away. I push my right leg forward. I'm still upright, but wobbly. Left leg next. Like using the Zimmer, but this time my hands are free. I find myself instinctively sticking them out, like a tightrope walker. I must look a complete fool. Grown man in pyjamas, playing at walking the wire.

I find my right hand and arm hovering over the bedside cabinet, then near the wall. Anywhere that offers support. This is stupid. Either I can walk, or I can't.

I force my hands down by my side. Pressure differentials seem to exist all over my body. I've bitten my lip with the strain of forcing my hand down, on the inside, thank God, where no one will see it, but it is bleeding. I taste the slightly sweet and sour, metallic salty taste of blood. I lurch forward, each step a battle with conflicting and uncontrollable pressures on my body, each single step a major decision.

I make it to the door. I've made it! Dare I put a hand out now? No! I half turn, half lurch round to go back to the bed, stumble, nearly fall over. I'm angry now, frustrated, tired. I've managed eight, perhaps nine steps. I can stumble across a few feet of ward on my own, painfully slowly. I can't write, I can't type, I can't pick up a cup or glass of liquid and guarantee to put its contents in my mouth. I'm still seeing double. My speech is still slurred. I'm going to be a wonderful asset to my wife, my family and friends.

I admit to myself something else I've known all day, but hidden from myself. I do a lot of public speaking in my job. At the age of 21 I was turned down for a Diploma of Education course at the University of Leeds because of an 'incurable stammer', or speech defect. That stammer had, in fact, been cured when I was 16, by an old Etonian called Burgess who had no medical qualifications but who had become so fed up with his own stammer that he'd invented a system and cured himself. He then offered a £100 course (a lot of money in 1965): money back if you weren't cured.

Burgess had cured the comedian Michael Bentine. He gave me the machinery to cure myself, but I'd become very tired revising flat-out for my finals and lazy about my speech when I went for the Dip.Ed. interview. I spoke badly. As a result I failed to get a place I dearly wanted, on the grounds that I would 'never be able to stand up in front of any group without making myself a laughing stock'. The words have stuck with me. There was less political correctness then. Now they would still have rejected me, but would never told me the real reason. The shock kick-started me in to full application of the Burgess system, and the stammer went away. Actually, the fear of stammering never leaves you, but no one sees that.

Now the stammer has come back, with force. Not enough to paralyse me, but enough to stop me in my verbal tracks over certain words. Only those closest to me would know.

Recuperation

Stammerers become clever. In the split second when they realise they're going to break into pieces on a word, they'll think of a substitute. Often the word will be as 'difficult' as the word they've stopped on, but the substitution does not give the brain the time to block it. I'd always known that stammering was psychological. Or thought I knew. Has there been some physiological damage in the brain to my speech centres? Do I, for the first time now have a physical cause for my stammer, rather than simply (simply?) a psychological one? I'm desperate for a picture of my brain, a map that will show what areas have been devastated and which are whole. It's weeks before I realise such a thing is called an MRI scan, and when I do eventually have one, it'll be full of surprises.

As for now, I'm restless, worried. Though I don't realise it, the long haul has just started. Being ill is no longer new, there's no adrenalin rush. The next few weeks will be the marathon of my life.

It is now nearing eleven o'clock. A new female patient has been admitted to the female half of the ward, the forbidden territory down the road. She's shouting, shrieking. At first it is simply a woman talking in a very loud voice. Apparently, I hear much later, she's sitting on the edge of the beds of various semi-comatose patients, talking and eventually shouting at them. I imagine most of the patients in the female ward are semi-comatose, as are most in the male ward. I've seen none of them on my Zimmer trips. Mind, I've seen no men either. Is this a geriatric ward I'm in? I don't know. It certainly seems to have no one who knows about strokes. Nor are we told about this noise, why it is going on for so long. I

83

can't understand why no one tries to quiet down the voice.

The shouting woman keeps it up until after one o'clock. By this time I'm screaming with frustration, wanting to get up and shout myself.

By 1.30am I'm still awake. There's a poem by Siegfried Sassoon, the First World War poet, which I suddenly remember. It's a moving meditation about a wounded man in a hospital ward, probably about this time of night:

He drowsed and was aware of silence heaped
Round him, unshaken as the steadfast walls.
Night, with a gust of wind, was in the ward,
Blowing the curtain to a glimmering curve.
Rain – he could hear it rustling through the dark;
Fragrance and passionless music woven as one;
Warm rain on drooping roses; pattering showers
That soak the woods; not the harsh rain that sweeps
Behind the thunder, but a trickling peace,
Gently and slowly washing his life away.

I wish suddenly I was a poet, or even a painter. And that I had Sassoon's silence. I note the extraordinary shadowed light from a dimmed-down bulb, shapes in the corners of the ward that take on a new meaning in the half-light, shapes that would frighten a child. The sound of gentle or troubled breathing coming from the three other patients, regular, soothing, almost hypnotic.

I start to remember Jaques and the Seven Ages of Man speech from *As You Like It*.

Recuperation

All the world's a stage,
And all the men and women merely players;
They have their exits and their entrances,
And one man in his time plays many parts,
His acts being seven ages. At first, the infant,
Mewling and puking in the nurse's arms.
Then the whining schoolboy, with his satchel
And shining morning face, creeping like snail
Unwillingly to school. And then the lover,
Sighing like furnace, with a woeful ballad
Made to his mistress' eyebrow. Then a soldier,
Full of strange oaths and bearded like the pard,
Jealous in honour, sudden and quick in quarrel,
Seeking the bubble reputation
Even in the canon's mouth. And then the justice,
In fair round belly with good capon lined,
With eyes severe and beard of formal cut,
Full of wise saws and modern instances;
And so he plays his part. The sixth age shifts
Into the lean and slippered pantaloon
With spectacles on nose and pouch on side;
His youthful hose, well saved, a world too wide
For his shrunk shank, and his big manly voice,
Turning again toward childish treble, pipes
And whistles in his sound. Last scene of all,
That ends this strange eventful history,
Is second childishness and mere oblivion,
Sans teeth, sans eyes, sans taste, sans everything.

(*As You Like It*, 2. 7. 139 – 167)

The Diary of a Stroke

Life is unthinking, dogged, automatic. It goes on until something absolutely massive forces it to stop. The three old men in this ward have nothing to live for except life itself. Their bones hurt, their bodies break. They cannot do for themselves the most basic things human beings need to do. In biological terms they are totally redundant. Yet they hang on, or rather that life force within them, hangs on. I doubt they have any control over it. It's as if that same life force drains something out of them: the other force, which might push them to take their own life, kills even the desire to die.

I think of all the things we do to make life beautiful, inspiring: music, art, literature. Yet life starts with a total, terrifying dependency, the screaming baby in the arms of whatever adult the lottery of genetics – and love or lust – has given it to. And then it ends with this dependency. How many people does it take to keep these old men alive? Where is their dignity?

I'm reminded of my mother, a proud woman, and the nursing home she went into with its ever-so faint smell of urine and cheap-perfumed disinfectant that no amount of cleaning could remove, the open bedroom doors with the old women looking yearningly out to see if anyone was coming for them. I remember one of my mother's rare flashes of insight, when she looked at me over her cigarette and says she knows that no one leaves places like this alive.

Age shall not wither them, the poem goes. Well, age certainly withered her, and it's withering me, and the others in this ward, and I want out of it before the withering becomes permanent. Finally I fall asleep, thoughts flashing around my head like the fluorescence round an oar-blade in a Scottish Highland sea.

Day 5

It is Monday morning. The weekend is over, and there is a new bustle and sense of purpose on the ward. It is as if it is waking up after a two-day sleep. Illness, it appears, acknowledges weekends and will slow down in order to accommodate the five days thou shalt work and the two days and a Friday evening thou shalt not. The ward is full of professional people who care, but apparently not on Saturday and Sunday.

The bustle is an interesting phenomenon to watch when you're stuck and static in bed. It consists of a lot of people walking around purposefully, with expressions of fixed determination on their faces. Quite what they are determined to do is less clear, and precious little of it seems to involve patients. We are like rocks around which the tide of people who work in this hospital ebb and flow. I pause at my choice of words. I said work *in* rather than work *for*. Humans have a touching need to be loyal to each other and to their place of work. One of things I always listen for when I visit a school is how the non-teaching staff describe the institution. There's a world of difference between the places where the workforce tell you they work *for* St Custard's, rather than just being employed there. Not many people are working for this hospital, I think. They're just in it.

They're missing a trick. Patients are scared, vulnerable, lonely. The mental equivalent of a hug, a good old fashioned bit of love, would have a phenomenal effect not only on the patients, but on those who served them. Surely any caring profession feeds on the dispensing of compassion, which breeds both respect and affection in return. That type of care runs two ways: the more that is given, the more that is received. The love you give is equal to the love you take. These staff could be worshipped by their patients if only they cared just a bit more; such an exchange would enrich mutual quality of life as much as better pay or conditions.

I'm lucky, with my family and with my employers. I'm getting more than my fair share of love and support. Yet I feel like the medieval prisoners in the Tower of London, whose quality of life depended totally on what friends or relations brought for them to eat and wear, without which they could starve or freeze to death.

This morning, I'm going to walk to the bathroom. I'm also going to carry my sponge bag, not cram it down the front of my pyjamas. I'm getting less scared about these trips, simply because I am learning to focus more and more, and there isn't room in my head for fear.

The macho thing would be to march down the centre of the corridor.

I decide not to be macho. I'll walk within a hand's reach of the wall, to steady myself in case I fall. Cowardice? Or prudence? Cowardly prudence, I decide.

The last thing I've been thinking about is ever writing

about what has happened to me. I don't do personal. I hide behind history, or poetry, or invented fictional characters who died a safe time ago. My hero is called Henry Gresham, and he's an amalgam of my sons and what I think Hamlet might have become if he hadn't died at the end of Act Five. He's been the central figure in four novels, with a fifth to come. Yet before this latest expedition, I do pause for personal thought. Would I ever be able to detail exactly what making this tiny walk was taking out of me? Surely it would just be an endless repetition of 'It was hard' and 'I did not like it'? How can you get across the twin, contrasting feelings, utter shame at being a cripple and a fierce exultation at being able to walk again, even if only for a few steps?

I, my razor and my face dice with death again. Gillette, if ever you want to use me, I'm free and available. At a price: I might not have a job any more. I'm glad I don't know exactly where the jugular is. Pleasure at being able to shave is now being replaced by frustration at not being able to hold the razor properly. It is still bending and turning in my hand like a live snake. I think about an electric razor. No! That's giving in! That's accepting disability! That's the way of defeat! If I shout loudly enough inside my own head, maybe I will silence my doubts.

That voice in my head, the one that is very, very tired and just wants to go back to bed, keeps playing like the drone on a bagpipe, always there despite the tune I'm trying to drown it out with.

I haven't tried to write again since the first disastrous experience. It's part of learning to cope. I'll have to hit the writing when I get out of this place, and instinctively I know it'll be easier in the book-lined study at home where I do my writing, or in our bolt hole, our home in Norfolk. It'll be normal to write in these rooms, and somehow the fact that I've written so much there will help me to get it back. I sense that it will hold out a carrot to me, not beat me with the stick of my failure. I must be getting better. I'm learning not to worry about things over which I have no immediate control.

Or is this part of a personality change?

Either way, it proves to be woefully self-deluding. Suddenly I'm reminded of something else I really don't want to remember, and this time I can't put it in the back drawer.

When I was 21, I was involved in a major accident, trying to rescue a much-loved cousin from a sea whipped up off the east coast of Scotland by a Force 10 gale. For several minutes I was face down, unconscious, in sea water. No one really knew how long my brain had been starved of oxygen. It can survive up to four minutes, perhaps even a bit longer if it is really cold. The amount of water in the lungs, the extent to which the casualty was breathing deep and oxygenating their blood before collapse, all play a part. It was edging over the four minute mark, and people who met me when I recovered knew that and obviously had 'brain damage' on their minds, or rather were wondering about how much I might have suffered. I learnt to recognise the rather haunted, nervous look in people's eyes as they advanced to shake my hand and welcome me back to the land of the living. I felt a massive urge to cross my eyes, start to dribble and fling my arms round them in a bear hug, mouthing 'wibbly wobbly, wibbly wobbly" at the same time ... I never did, of course.

Now I was worried that people would think stroke equals personality change. Hang on. Never mind about other people. How on earth could *I* know if I'd changed? Surely if the brain changes it accepts what is there as being normal? So if I had scrunched up personality areas of the brain, presumably I'd think I'd always been like that.

I remembered from a Reith Lecture the story of the navvy building railways – or was it canals? To blast away rock, a hole was drilled into the cliff and explosive tamped down at one end. A steel or iron rod was used for this, and if the user was careless it could strike a spark, igniting the explosive and turning the hole into the barrel of a gun and the rod in to the bullet. This had happened to an American called Phineas Gage in the 19th century, and the steel rod shot through his head. Fortunately, if there could be any good fortune in such a thing, the rod left the hole with a very high muzzle velocity. In other words it was travelling very, very fast. It stayed lodged in his skull – but, astonishingly, he survived. This is good news if a high-velocity bullet hits you. The exit wound is only slightly larger than the entry wound, whereas a low-velocity bullet, particularly a lead one, travelling that bit more slowly flattens on impact and forces an increasingly larger hole in the flesh and bone it moves through. It does this not just through its flattening, but because of the tearing shock waves it sends ahead of itself in the fluid that is our flesh. So this man had a

91

neat hole drilled through his head and part of his brain. He lived. Not only that, but he recovered. Except he was a different person, a criminal personality as it happened.

Had I changed? I felt the same. But then I would, wouldn't I?

Part of the problem, I am thinking, is that I will now think that people are looking for major changes in me. I will therefore strive to be normal. But, of course, one does not strive to be normal under normal circumstances. One just *is* normal. This is what lets so many people down at interview. The minute you try to be normal you send out a false signal, and appear abnormal. It's Catch 22.

Sometimes, I think, this whole thing verges on farce. Except I doubt that anyone who has had a stroke ever died of laughing.

Well, there's only one thing for it. I'll have to ask my wife and whichever of my sons is on duty today if I appear to them to be the same personality they knew before the stroke. It's not exactly a fair question. I still slur my speech, and occasionally have a stammer that last troubled me 35 years ago. I am having to focus on small things, often physical, that I've not had to think about for years. I'm hardly in a normal frame of mind. I don't know whether I'll still have a job at the end of all this, and am too uninformed to know that a rather more important question is whether or not I will suffer another, perhaps massive, stroke. At the moment, my only medication is aspirin. It thins the blood and makes a clot less likely. But I've been taking aspirin since I had cancer. Much good it did me. They can't prescribe anything stronger for a week or so, in case all that stands between my brain and a blood leakage is a clot. Dissolving the clot too early with a more powerful medication, before the lining has time to regenerate, could be like the boy on the dyke pulling his finger out. End of civilisation as we know it.

There aren't too many answers here, only too many problems. I resolve them by walking – *walking* – to the bathroom. I feel as if there should be a man with a red flag walking in front of me, and a red light and bleeping siren on my head, similar to those they use when lorries reverse.

I bash into the wall five times on the outward journey but I make it.

And I do not slash my throat with the razor. Job done. I feel a sense of satisfaction roughly equivalent to that I felt when I was awarded my Ph.D.

On the way back I bash into the wall seven times. I choose to ignore the constant bashing, and the fact that my compass has been mis-set by 45°. My body wants to walk like a crab, sideways. I aim for the middle of the door and hit the door jamb bang on. My missile is clearly unguided, but at least I'm flying and getting (eventually) to where I want to go. As I stumble back to my bed, I start learning to aim for an area 45° to the right of where I actually want to go. If I do that, I end up dead centre. If I don't, I end up 45° to the left of my aiming point.

My wife arrives, looking tired. I tell her that I can walk, that I have walked that morning. She doesn't believe me, I can see. She was still steadying me in my Zimmer yesterday. So I have to show her, pathetically proud of my little victory.

I walk to the door, very slowly, and walk back to the bed. My left foot catches on my right ankle as I look up to smile at her, and I nearly spoil it by falling over as I turn. My wife looks pleased, but also rather unbelieving. I realise afterwards that she can see just how very, very wobbly I am. I am too full of pleasure at regaining some independence to realise how little I have actually gained. She hovers by me as I go, very slowly, ten steps down the corridor. I am going to do this all day, I decide, repeat the endless series of sorties we did with the Zimmer. My wife is less certain, I suspect she's just waiting for me to have my first fall. As with so much else, she exudes confidence and calm. Thirty-eight years after we first met, there are still parts of each other that we don't know. But I know enough to sense what she is repressing.

Today Mr Frankland is being sent home. I don't know what's wrong with him. No doctor ever seems to come near him. I suspect he's just worn out. He's also quite deaf and forgetful. He's had it explained to him that he's going home this morning, but he's forgotten this already, or chosen not to remember.

He likes hospital, he tells me in one of his rare moments of lucidity.

'The food's good, isn't it, bearing in mind what they have to cope with?'

I shudder to think what poor old Mr Frankland will be eating when he gets home if, by comparison, NHS-mash or mess, tastes good.

Mr Frankland, I suspect, would like to take up residence

in the ward. His social worker is a middle-aged Asian man, and he's a saint, one of the very few I've met so far in my journey. He's trying to tell Mr Frankland that he's going home.

'You're going home. Mr Frankland,' he keeps saying patiently. Mr Frankland is deaf, so it's not the social worker's fault that the decibel levels are somewhere near those of a Harrier at take off.

'No I'm not,' says Mr Frankland, firmly at first, and then more in hope than in expectation.

'Do you live in house or a flat, Mr Frankland,' the social worker asks.'

'What?'

'Do you live in a house or a flat?'

'What's that?'

'House or a flat?'

'I live in a house.'

'Has it got stairs, Mr Frankland?'

'Hairs?'

'No, stairs, Mr Frankland.'

Pause.

'Of course it's got fucking stairs. I fell down 'em. That's why I'm in hospital.'

It's funny, at first. Then I think of Mr Frankland, alone, in his house with stairs, with a state pension – the greatest highlight of his life waiting for social services or the home help to call.

To this day I've no knowledge of what happened to Mr Frankland. That simple instance of selfish disregard still gives me bad dreams.

Thoughts are coming back to me now. It sounds daft,

but for most of my life, thoughts have been pushing at me inside my head, like people jostling, pushing to come forward in a queue. I've learnt to shout orders at them, put them in some sort of order. It usually works, but I've always had the tendency to go semi-detached, as my family call it, particularly in social situations where I'm bored. I leave part of me in the social situation, while the rest of me is thinking about something more interesting. As if to compensate for this, at times I'm obsessive, clutching on to one idea, issue or thought and refusing to let it go until I've reached a solution for it, even if the moment and the rest of the world have passed it by.

The stroke has been a very unusual experience in more ways than one. Rather than several thoughts crying out for attention, the obsessive mode has dominated. Stand up. Control that hand. Fix that speech. One, single and obsessive idea has tended to occupy my head at any given time. This has been very unusual and rather unsettling. I've become accustomed to the inside of my head switching between something like a noisy customs hall at an airport and a one-to-one interview in a police interview room, and now I, or my head, or my brain, have got stuck in the one-to-one situation. Now, at last, normal service is being (partly) returned. There's knocking at the door of the police cell and others wanting to come in.

So my mind throws up a memory from when I was fourteen or fifteen, and away at the boarding school which I hated. We had started community service in the mad, bad 1960s. No doubt the school had gone to the local vicar or whatever, got a list of deserving old people and attached pupils to visit them. I doubt in those days much checking up was done. We had to fend for ourselves rather at school, something I don't say in support of *laissez-faire* attitudes. Most of the people I've met who say that they were thrashed/starved/sodomised to death at school and it never did them any harm actually seem severely damaged to me.

Back to the 1960s. I was sent as a child on my first community service afternoon to a nauseous back yard that was clearly a lavatory for most of the dogs in the village and some of the adults too. I was to ring a doorbell and meet the elderly gentleman who, I imagined, would delight in a visit from a posh kid. Dream on, dumb child. The yard would have been a superb setting for Fagin's Den in *Oliver Twist*. What was I expecting? Not much from this or any experience at that time in my life, if I'm being frank. I didn't have many expectations then, but reckoned glumly that things would turn out worse than I had ever imagined. I was not disappointed. I began to panic when there was no answer after the fifth, long ring on the dirty doorbell. That deep sense of realism that is a part of childhood knew that somehow, inevitably, it would be my fault if I failed to make contact. It always was my fault, then. For anything. What I wasn't expecting was that at the sixth ring a gnarled, old male head that looked like one of the more grotesque gargoyles from one of our older cathedrals would fling open a window, and yell:

'Fuck off, you little bastard, or I'll set the dog on you!'

I began to feel sympathy for Jehovah's Witnesses. It wasn't the dog that frightened me (it began to bark as its master shouted, and the bark sounded like a bloodthirsty howl). I'd been brought up with dogs. You knew where you were with them, unlike humans. It was first the use of the 'f' word. We simply didn't say it then, on fear of death. It was the loss of my 'f' word virginity. Secondly, I was damned if this old bugger was going to get me caned. Rather feebly, with hindsight, I called out,

'They'll punish me if I don't see you! I've been sent by the school.'

I really wasn't expecting the answer.

'Oh Christ! Another bloody victim!'

Pause.

'I eat little bastards like you for breakfast. Now bugger off!'

I think I must have met the original for the old man in the *Adrian Mole* stories. I saved my skin by the best possible method when I reported in to base, by simply telling the truth. You didn't mention the 'f' word to authority in those days. I was rather proud of myself when I said instead that the old man I had disturbed had used 'physical' words and threatened to kill me. Next week I was given a rather sweet old lady. No one said sorry, of course. If you didn't mention the 'f' word to authority, authority never mentioned the 's' word ('sorry') either.

Here and now, Mr Frankland would have given his eye teeth for a young person to come calling twice a week. I doubted he would be so lucky. We've made old age such a condition to be ashamed of. And we have encouraged our young to look forward, and not realise that a sane world looks both forwards and backwards.

The physiotherapist finally came to see me. Female.

Young. Efficient. Attractive. Busy, in the way that so many of her age are. She was economical with words, far too professional to drum her fingers on the clipboard as she talked at me. Yet somehow she conveyed the fact that she was busy, busy, busy, that there were many other patients waiting to be talked at, and so little time to talk at them. If I stayed in the area, I could get physiotherapy in … a fortnight or more.

I came to realise that in the NHS 'a fortnight or more' was the equivalent of the taxi dispatcher's 'With you in five minutes'. In other words, it expressed a vague ambition that could in no way be interpreted as a commitment.

Among other things, she suggested closing my eyes and trying to place my forefinger on the tip of my nose. Ouch, I said, as the first attempt plunged in to my left eye.

If you stay in the hospital, she said, we can send you to Rehab.

If I was a dog, my hackles would have risen. Rehab? Stay in the hospital? I simply did not wish to be Mr Frankland. Rehab to me was black and white films of the Second World War, where Douglas Bader lost patience with his artificial leg, and everyone was unfailingly cheerful. And if rehab was what I thought it was, I'd rather do self-help. *I had to get out of this place!*

There was another reason I had to go: the cheerfulness in hospitals. Sustained and artificial cheerfulness can be the most exhausting thing on earth, after falling in love. I'd always found a really good row a wonderful way of sustaining a relationship. Wasn't there a medical equivalent? Or the equivalent of having a really good cry when someone you love dies? How cathartic would it have been if every now and again the doctors and the nurses had come in with long faces and said, 'the truth of it, Martin, is that you're buggered, pretty broke and busted, and there's a great deal of uncertainty around about whether or not we, or anyone else, can mend you'.

I was going semi-detached again. Personality change? Or personality reinforcement? Perhaps the personality does not change after a stroke, but certain aspects that were there before become stronger? Semi-detached was OK. I was used to that. I'd better be careful not to make it to a lone house out in the country.

'I'd like to go home,' I announce firmly.

Much pursing of lips, furrowing of brows.

'Well ... can you walk down stairs? Are there stairs in your home?'

Sudden sense of *deja vu.*

'There are ... stairs,' I say truthfully. 'Really easy, wide and shallow stairs,' I lie glibly. 'And a housekeeper who comes in every day. Well ... someone we hardly know comes in for some hours a week to do some cleaning. And the house can be set up with a bedroom downstairs so I don't even need to go upstairs.'

'They'll ask you to walk up and down the stairs here,' the physio says, 'tomorrow, before they can let you out.'

They. The Stalinist Hospital Police, adopting a terrifying Catch 22 situation. *We propose to do nothing useful with you while you're here except let you rot, but we're damned if we're going to let you out.*

And we'll need to sort out a few details about what level of care there is at home... I detect a steely glint in my

100

Recuperation

wife's eyes. If they're challenging her capacity to care they're starting a battle they can't win. She follows the physiotherapist out (who hasn't actually given me any exercises), tells her she is taking me home and will organise rehab herself.

It's after lunch. My wife is seated by the bedside, reading. Suddenly she looks up.

'Do you remember my father?' she asks innocently.

Her father had a stroke in his 70s, one that went undiagnosed for 12 weeks. He was fine lying down, but lost all sense of balance when he put his head up. He was incapable of standing and became bed-bound. He could do *The Times* crossword lying down, but didn't know what was in his sponge bag if he sat up.

My father-in-law is a bit special. He fought through the whole of the Second World War at the sharp end, and did up a semi-ruined house in the wild Highlands of Scotland virtually on his own. One of my abiding memories is of a 70 year-old man, who earlier that day had well and truly beaten me in a race up a Scottish hillside to do some fishing, walking casually along the roof ridge of his Scottish house, just like the posters of the building workers standing, or sitting, on a steel beam above New York in the 1930s. He's a gentle man, my father-in-law, but with a latent Scottish toughness, which comes from having to fight for much when he was young, and take nothing for granted. It was the gardening, I suspect, that made him fight his stroke. The loss of his sense of balance meant he could no longer dig or stand in his garden. Life without gardening would be no life at all for him, and he wasn't ready to die yet.

The Diary of a Stroke

And then there is my mother-in-law. A geologist at heart, she has what appears to be a gentle personality that, you discover, is actually rather like the gentle tendrils of water that creep into a house with a flood, totally and deceptively unstoppable. Rather like a younger Miss Marple, she has a tenacity that makes Araldite look positively soppy. She studied strokes on the Internet and came up with a programme for my father-in-law based on recent American research and practice. Among other things, it required him to sit up in bed opposite a wall, chuck a tennis ball and catch it as it bounced back. Hand eye co-ordination and balance seem crucially linked. The problem with this routine was that, certainly early on, my father-in-law did not catch the ball. He dropped it regularly. The result was that my indomitable mother in law had to scuttle around like a latter-day ball boy at Wimbledon, though one also in her 70s.

I'd picked up a jokey, hand-sized rugby ball from the conference I was attending, one of those things that you were meant to squeeze to relieve stress.

'Let's see if you can catch it,' my wife says. She moves to the end of the bed. She throws the ball at me. Some seconds after it has flown past me ear, one of my hands responds. On this showing I could have been picked as England's goalkeeper.

I laugh, hollowly.

We try again. This time I make a spasmodic gesture with both hands and knock the ball up into the air and against the gantry that supports the TV screen.

My ball exercises remind me of something. I used to do a lot of white-water canoeing. When you are trying

102

to go up a rapid, as distinct from simply following it down, there are times when you seem merely to be holding your own in the foaming water, while in fact you're advancing a couple of inches a time. To make it through, you simply have to lock down all systems, concentrate totally on the paddles, and ignore the pain. There is no pain, of course, with this challenge. There are no pain receptors in the brain, which is why there is no pain with a stroke. But, apart from that, the rugby ball challenge is surprisingly similar.

We giggle a lot and have to give up eventually because the damned thing is skittling around all over the ward, forcing my wife to go under the beds of the old men dying on the other side of the ward. Fifty times, we try, or thereabouts; twenty-five her throwing it me, twenty-five my throwing it back. I catch it not at all.

I start to get interested, despite the outward failure. First, my father-in-law invented, or had invented for him by his wife, what was in effect a training regime. He is now back on his feet, driving, walking, gardening, and his handwriting is exactly as it was before his stroke. The regime worked for him, although it took two years. Second, there is at least an element of fun in trying to catch a tennis ball. Playing catch was invented by humans about the same time as making love; it's virtually a genetic drive, for men at least. Third, I am beginning to wonder about the whole question and answer routine. Clearly I am firing neurons around in my brain to try and catch the rugby ball. Most of the time it isn't working. I'm dropping it. But what if firing those commands off is like driving away at a rock fall in a mine, beating a path through the rubble that has crashed down and blocked it? What if merely *asking* my brain to do something it cannot do is setting it a challenge to learn to do it again? If that's true, even a *dropped* ball is an achievement, pushing me that little extra bit up the river, along the path to recovery.

I have to make such exercises work for me, too. But it's never going to happen in hospital. There's no room, for starters, and men careering around after bouncing tennis balls will upset the rhythm of the ward more than a bit. Perhaps they do things like this in rehab, but how would that work? I will have an appointment, an hour-long slot, and it will allow for lunch breaks and tea breaks and be when the rehab unit finds it convenient.

But the bureaucracy of the hospital ignores the individual, me. I am bursting with energy one minute, exhausted the next. The stamina needed to do any form of exercise comes and goes, and it is crucial that when it comes I can use it. Rehab will presumably force me into a time strait-jacket, as well as giving me their routines rather than the ones I am working out do me the most good.

I just have to get home, build up my own little rehab unit round me.

It is a bizarre feeling, this need to get home. It is like that first night when the blackness came, the overwhelming urge to get away, to retreat and lick wounds, to be left on my own to solve it. I wonder about the single room versus ward issue. I can see people get lonely on their own, and of course, it is vastly more expensive to build and inefficient to supervise. But I think at least some of my tiredness is because I often feel like an animal in a zoo in this public ward, except my cage is my bed and there are no bars on it.

Anyway, first things first. Can I manage the bloody stairs? They're not going to let me go home tomorrow unless I can walk up and down some stairs. Time to try it out.

I call it walking, but it's not. I can just about stand up, but this huge sea-like surging motion when I do is no less strong than it first was. I don't tell them anything, of course, and anyway, they don't ask. Oddly, this makes it harder to stand still than to try and move. The walking is strange. One foot, the right one, will push itself forward, but the other foot will only come half the way, so it is as if I am dragging my leg. I am leading with one foot all the time. More worryingly, I still cannot steer a straight line. Whatever I do, I veer to the left, usually at a 45° degree angle. This is really annoying, as I keep walking into the sides of doors on the very few trial runs I have had, even though I am trying to compensate. There is a difference from the first time. Now, I do not hit the side of the door frame full-on, but catch it with my shoulder or my hip. It hurts.

There is a T-junction half way along the corridor that leads to the stairs and out. If, when I arrive at the junction and have to turn right in to the corridor, I aim at the right-hand wall I will probably end up by the left-hand wall, which will be fine. But there is a double door at the end of the corridor. For some reason I know that I will only be able to go down a few stairs if I can have the wall on my right-hand side. If I walk to the stairs it will take hours. I'm going to find it difficult to invent a reason for wanting to cross to the other side. Yet I'm going to blow it if I have to walk down the stairs on the left.

There has to be an answer.

We have a conference of war. We evolve a Cunning Plan.

I walk far better earlier on in the day. After even a short walk, I am exhausted. My performance deteriorates rapidly as the day progresses. Presumably the same will be true of my stair-walking capacity. This is our plan.

We will plead for the stair test to be done in the morning, so my wife or son can drive me home in daylight. There is no logical reason why daylight is better than night time, but it sounds good. We will move Heaven and earth to discover what time in the morning the physio and nurse will do the test. I will do no walking before the stair test, conserving my energy, making this the first run of the day, whenever it comes. To avoid tiring myself out, I will go to the day room on my Zimmer at least half an hour before test time, and sit there with a book. *The day room is right by the stairs – and it is on the right-hand side!* This is crucial. It means I won't have tired myself out before the test. I'll be on the right side of the ward, literally and figuratively, to go down the stairs with the rail to hang on to on my right. I can probably fudge crossing the small stair-well space at the bottom, so I can walk up with the rail clutched in my right hand as well.

None of this adequately explains why I'm spending so much time trying to outwit the NHS, instead of leaning on it for support. I'm playing *I'm A Patient Get Me Out*

Of Here. There's something rotten in all this, and for once I don't think it's in me.

'Shouldn't you try walking down the stairs now?' my wife asks.

Of course I must. But I'm tired now, and it's a long walk to the doors and the start of the stairs. But too much rests on my passing this test tomorrow. How will my confidence be if the test is my first experience of stairs? But I have to do it. I keep on being reminded of endless airplane films where the pilots are running out of fuel and report that they're flying on air – and hope, pluck and everything else that made us win the Battle of Britain. Pluck? You must be joking? All the 'plucky' ones had was a capacity to hide fear, not wand it away. Stiff upper lip and don't let anyone see you've got the shakes. I'm reaching down in to my reserve tanks time after time, and the fear grows that one day I'll reach and there'll be nothing left, and the plane will fall out of the sky.

I have to get to the stairs, of course. It's painfully slow, and, to my surprise, quite physically painful. I suspect the pain is not because my muscles have atrophied, though they must have, at least a little, but because I am standing at such odd angles that muscles I've never used are being called into play to keep me upright and lurch me forward. The pain is their way of complaining. My wife is anxious, hanging by my shoulder, clearly worried I will fall down. Or steer so bloody badly that I walk straight out through a window, I mutter to myself.

I am fed up today. My wife adds to it by telling me that I'm walking like a duck. I know I am, with my feet splayed out for balance. I get revenge for her telling the truth by being nasty to her. I make some comments that I think are funny and cutting. Only in bed that night do I realise they are pathetic and wholly unjustified.

Walking down the stairs has an extraordinary moment. When my foot is one or two inches above the stair, I seem to lose it off my radar. There is a brief moment when the foot is dropping on to the stair right enough, but only through gravity, not through any muscular control. It is scary, but apparently unavoidable.

We open the door. It's something of a seminal moment. That door keeping me from the outside world was achieving mythic, symbolic proportions. And now we've just opened it. The world beyond the ward beckons.

It's going to be very interesting when I really get through that door. The tiny world of a hospital ward may drive you mad, but it can let you concentrate on the matter in hand. The minute I'm out of that door, I'm back in the real world. The world that will decide if I'll recover fully. I won't be able to keep those issues at bay, as I can partly do now.

The stairs are an anti-climax. They're certainly not easy, but with total concentration and a painfully slow pace, they can be done. They swim up and down alarmingly, but as long as I put my foot down on a down surge and rest for the upsurge in my sea-sick head, I can do it.

'Well done,' my wife says.

'We did it,' I say. I think of all the people who have to fight these battles on their own, and I suddenly feel very small, and very, very grateful.

When my wife goes I feel empty. A strange, febrile silence descends on the ward. The patients have all been fed, watered and emptied, and lie like wrapped bodies in the morgue in their hospital beds. I suppose I should feel lonely. All I do feel is a strange exhaustion. The nearest I can come to describing it is as if I was trapped in an underground car park, with hundreds of cars running their engines, gasping for breath in the polluted air. Whatever I do, however hard I breathe, there is just not enough oxygen to sustain me, but enough to stop me losing consciousness. I am an engine deprived somehow of fuel. Here in my bed, alone at night, the smoke and fumes are all around me, surrounding me, numbing my responses. It would be so easy to give up.

I lie in bed and gaze at the night light. It is still two lights, not one. Will this nightmare never end? Am I just fooling myself that I'll get better?

Day 7

Dawn. Grey light over an industrial landscape of
minimalist modern buildings. Somewhere behind that
stained concrete, behind all the little windows, are the
future men and women who'll be born today, and men
and women who'll die today and become the past. In
between the two extremes will be people praying to die
and people praying to live, plus many who are very
confused and simply don't know what's happening to
them, or whether they want to live or die.

Looking after them will be the nurse who's just had
an abortion and the nurse who's crying as she talks in
to a mobile and tells her man that the fertilisation treatment
has worked, at last; on the team too is the registrar who's
just heard he's going to be a consultant and the doctor
who can no longer ignore his own symptoms and wishes
he hadn't for so long.

Time for the morning routine. And how are we today?
I realise that only one of the staff has ever asked me
how I am. It was the Fat Consultant and he carried on
his speech to his acolytes before I could have possibly
answered, even if I'd been capable of it or wanted to.
Never mind asking how I am.

No one has asked me who I am, or what I do when

Recuperation

I'm not lying like a sack of potatoes in this bed. I wonder if the first NHS hospitals had a standard issue of pyjamas, like a prisoner's uniform. One thing is certain: this hospital will never be found guilty of worshipping the cult of the individual.

A rare spark of humanity is shown by the lady who brings round the trolley with papers and other goodies on it. She smiles at me, comments on my choice of newspaper. The contents of the trolley are basic. No *Guardian* or *Daily Telegraph*, just the *Mirror* and the *Sun*. No organic muesli bars, just Mars Bars. Rather downmarket. The lady is charming, kind and interested. I suspect her trolley has built up a debt to rival that England owed the USA after the Second World War. She is not the sort of person to refuse an old man a bag of sweets because he does not happen to have the money on him. I hope someone is as kind to her when her turn comes round.

Time for the morning report and review.

Bad news: speech still slurred; vision crap; balance crap; writing and typing skills nil; hand-eye co-ordination dire; control over hands crap; breakfast goes everywhere except my mouth.

Good news: personality maybe not OK, but apparently as before; I can walk, sort of; vision may be double, but it was quadruple; it seems to get *just* a little better every day – or is that wishful thinking? Spirit is bloody but still unbowed; haven't had second, fatal stroke. At least, not yet.

How are you, Martin?

Do you know the definition of an English gentleman? An English gentleman is a person who when you ask

111

him 'How are you?' keeps his answer short and uninformative.

How am I? I'm fine.

The memory that comes unsummoned this time is of endless submarine films. I love the German *Das Boot* which is the story of a German U-boat in the Second World War. The boat sinking, out of control, plunging to well below design depth. The crew looking hopelessly at their depth gauge as it reaches and goes beyond maximum. The huge cracking noises in the hull. The inevitable spurt of water into a compartment, somehow closed off by a man wielding what looks like a huge spanner.

They are all going to die. And then, the speed of descent starts to slow, and stops, and the submarine hangs there, way below the depth at which its hull should have been crushed. Will there be one massive implosion? Or will the sub slowly start to rise?

HMS *Me* has definitely been holed and probably should have sunk. It did descend rapidly, for quite a while, and its commander thought he was a goner. Now it seems to be hanging in there, at a very dangerous depth.

The astute reader will have noticed that I have so far compared myself to a plane running out of fuel, a spluttering engine and now a leaky submarine. My unconscious clearly thinks I'm a machine. Can the man machine fix itself?

I'm under no illusions. I've stabilised, that's all. I may even have bounced up a little after having hit the bottom with a massive crash, but that doesn't mean I'm on the way up. My time in hospital has allowed me to sink no further, that's all. It's actually been damn all use in telling me how to get back to the surface.

Recuperation

The tricks my wife and I have rehearsed for the physio work. I manage the five stairs. Interestingly, going down is far harder than coming up. When our dog was a puppy it had the classic great round tum and little short legs. There were three steps down from the kitchen to the garden. It would look morosely at the steps, then gingerly start to go down them. Suddenly the weight of its rear end would start pushing it forward. An expression of panic would come to its eyes as it suddenly found itself overtaken by its bottom, and it would tumble on to the path, legs splayed out everywhere. I am terrified that I will fall down the stairs. That regular, surging movement still dominant inside my head becomes seriously threatening when looking down a flight of stairs, trying to throw me forwards.

There is much umm-ing and aah-ing on the ward. I thought the NHS was desperate for beds. Yet they seem inclined to keep me in. I'll only add to the problem if I say what I want to say, that this place is keeping me ill, not curing me. I exaggerate the amount of help available to me, manage to stay calm. I forget to tell them my wife works full time. Well, they didn't ask the question...

The medical profession does not seem very involved in the, for me, crucial question of my discharge.

They let me out. My wife can be very persuasive. I think they're scared of her.

The best fun I've had in recent days has been taking a shower. I'm now having my second bit of fun. I'm putting on clothes again, real clothes. It seems to take hours, and it does, but I'm determined to do it on my own. Buttons on my shirt are almost impossible. They have not only developed personalities but an impish desire to ever-so-nearly go in the hole – and then slide out. I feel the frustration welling up inside me. I've noted it as one of the main features of a stroke, a destructive anger born of frustration. I must watch it. The temptation is to take it out on other people.

Finally, I'm dressed. You've done well, the ward staff say. I have to remind myself that they are decent people. It's not their fault that nothing said or done here has seemed to help me recover. I've been parked, that's all. There's a real pleasure at seeing someone actually walk out of the ward. I wonder if their pleasure is not simply a function of how many people they see carried out in a box. I forget that it is nurses who prepare and wrap the corpse before the porters take it to the morgue. Doing that day in and day out must build up a self-protecting skin, a type of survival-insensitivity. If you need to protect yourself against the dead, how do you remain as open as you need to be towards the living?

I walk down to the lift this time. No stairs, thank you. It's harder this time to walk, but I'm buoyed up by excitement. The excitement is working in part to break my concentration, and the instant I stop putting all my mind on walking I start to stumble. I'm walking very, very slowly.

I see the door. The door opens.

Suddenly, I'm free. Prison break! The door shuts behind me. I'm out.

A caustic voice inside my head wonders if they'll notice that I've vanished off the ward. I am sorely tempted to find two fag butts, light them, and leave one smouldering in each of my slippers, placed carefully by the bed as if I'd just been in them. Would two slightly smoking slippers make them think a hand had reached up from the nether regions and dragged me down there?

We're outside now. I'm tasting fresh air for the first time in six days. Real air, rather than cooped-up-inside-a-badly-designed-building-with-ill-people air. It's wonderful. The day is sunny, cold, a few white clouds scudding across a blue sky. A kerb stone is a major hurdle to be plotted, navigated and conquered. I'm determined not to use a stick, and never ever want to see a Zimmer frame again.

For the first time since it happened I have an unselfish thought. My wife must be exhausted, physically and emotionally. She has a long drive ahead of her.

'Let's have a cup of tea before we start', I say.

'Can't you make it to the car?' she asks.

'Yes', I reply, but I'm worried about once I'm in it.

The café for the hospital is on our route. It's empty, and a bored looking woman is swiping at stainless steel and glass behind the counter, showing all the enthusiasm I – and my wife, for that matter – feel for ironing. Still, it's the first clean place I've seen in the hospital. We order tea, and I sit down. The café looks out on to a central foyer and reception area. You can see why so many TV series have been based in hospitals. A con man could have a dream of a time here. Any man with a suit, shirt and tie is afforded doctor status, which in hospital is significantly closer to God than most people get without going through the bother of dying, and the waves open before him or her.

The real interest is the patients. There are a number of young men with things broken – arms, legs – parading about. Of the older people, a large number are seriously overweight. There are always at least three staff having a quick fag outside by the entrance, but I'm intrigued by the number of patients and relatives doing the same thing. It's one of the rare times that the patient/staff apartheid is breached, as they huddle round a fag that will land them both in hospital regardless of how well, or how badly, qualified they are.

I suddenly realise how I must look, hunched over a table with a cup of tea that I can't guide to my mouth, and I don't like it. I run my hand through my hair, push my shoulders back.

The dog is in the back of the car. He is a black Labrador, which means he has a simple outlook on life. He is mightily confused. He looks up at me, pleading with his eyes as Princess Diana did when she wanted to look both vampish and vulnerable, showing the whites and looking up. His tail half-heartedly, if a tail can be half-hearted, makes a motion that never quite turns into a wag. He's been taken out of his routine. As an animal with a natural desire to please, he doesn't know what he's meant to do, or what his role is. I sympathise. His bed is in the back of the car, and he knows the car. He's determined not to leave it.

The car is quite low. When I start to sit down, I have control of my body for about the first third of the movement. After that, I become like the space shuttle at landing, no engine power and only the force of my own momentum. I don't really want to hit the car seat like a

1,000lb bomb, particularly as my head is likely to collide with the car roof if I do so.

I stand with my back to the open door, grip the roof and lower myself down. It's exactly the same thing that happened with my foot going down stairs. The muscles collapse two-thirds of the way through, but I hit the car seat with less than the speed of sound and my head still attached to my neck. Embarrassingly – I look round to see if anyone is looking, but the Third World War could just have been declared in the car park for all the interest anyone's showing – I have to lift each leg into the seat well, picking it up like a package and depositing it.

It's a good feeling, to be dressed in my own clothes, driving out of the hospital. I start to chat to my wife, and the next thing I know I'm turning in to where I live. I've fallen asleep dramatically, undergoing some sort of cut-out mechanism. God knows what effect my sudden vanishing off the face of the conscious universe must have had on my wife.

I feel as if I've been away for a very long time. Home seems reassuring but slightly alien at the same time. Is it because I've been yearning so hard and so long to get there? Or is it because in my sub-conscious I never thought I would get there again?

The next few hours are a blur. I wander round the house slowly, very slowly, and touch things, as if to prove that they're still there. At the back of my mind is the thought that with only a little more bad luck, this is a place I might never have seen again. The stairs are narrow, and have a sharp turn in them. I can get up them if I put the same foot forward each time, the right foot, and drag the left after it on to the same step. That ruddy left hand side again. It's easier to crawl up them on my knees like a supplicant, and I allow myself one day, one day only, to do this before I stick to two legs again. As for coming down ... I decide that for a while at least I will be coming down the stairs on my bottom, one step at a time. Is this giving in to my illness? I persuade myself that it's simply marshalling resources. When I tell myself I can't believe that, I decide it's a reward, a treat I will give myself for having got this far.

My wife and I sit down together. It is early evening. I cannot make a cup of tea, trust my rebellious hands with a hot kettle, mug or cup. This is clearly a priority. Life without tea and coffee is unthinkable. I can feed myself, if I wrap myself round with tea towels. We start to work out a rehab programme.

The easiest thing would be to sit at home and vegetate, be ill, become a permanent patient. I'm tired now, really tired. Simple things, like getting out of a car, leave me exhausted. I need to know one simple thing, or rather one simple thing with a number of offshoots.

Will I be permanently disabled?

Will I make a full recovery? If the truth is somewhere between the two, will the level of my disability allow me to do my job at an acceptable level, acceptable both to me and to my employers? I'm by nature very impatient. Even I can see that the answer to this question will take a few weeks to find out.

I don't know yet that stroke victims often make significant progress early on as swelling in the brain dies down, and then stick fast, improving no more. I do know that I can't yet go on proper medication, and at the back of both my mind and that of my wife, is the lurking fear of the second stroke.

We don't talk about it. We both know it is there. My father died of a coronary, at the age of 74, but somehow I've persuaded myself that he died of a stroke. It sounds daft to mention it now, but I'm writing this diary not to make it credible or dramatic, but simply as I remember things and thoughts happening to me. I knew he'd been hit twice by heart attacks. He remained conscious and lucid after the first, but suffered a second fatal attack a day later. It's strange that my mind had locked this away. His death was one of the seminal moments in my life, as I suspect the death of a parent is to any human being. He was a good man, my father, who'd largely made his own good fortune, was possessed of vast integrity and had intelligence, a wicked sense of humour and an extraordinary capacity to keep his feet on the ground.

As it was, I'd also had a stroke and was on the same dose of aspirin I'd been administering to myself before it all happened. Whatever had caused that stroke was still there, and in the most dramatic way possible, my body had shown me that it was, at least, now prone to this sort of thing. Has it developed lasting damage? I am still well within the time frame to find out.

We start to work out our own rehabilitation programme, my wife and I. Going to bed, my own bed, washing in my own bathroom, breaks something down within me. I start to cry. It is the first and only time I cry throughout the whole business. I hate myself for this display of emotion, and cannot control it. It passes.

The Diary of a Stroke

My wife and three sons react to this in the same manner as they have reacted to everything that has happened. There are things too personal to write about even in a personal story, and how can you write about something that has no physical form and precious few words? It is simply the power of love, and it leaves me with my self-respect intact.

Why am I writing all this down, some time around midnight as summer is launching? I'm writing it because my long-standing literary agent heard the basic version of my story, and said you must publish this, so other people know what a stroke is like. Not because it will sell lots, not because it will boost sales of your other books. But because other people should know what it's like to have a stroke. I love my agent dearly. She's suddenly turned from ITV to BBC. From being a delightfully commercial person to a public service person. Is it too stupid and insufferably pompous to think that telling the story of what happened to me might actually help someone else?

Well, in the unlikely event of that being true, the story has come to a watershed. A lot is going to happen in the next two weeks. But here I am, having released myself from hospital and facing the second-greatest challenge in my life. Have I learnt anything that could help someone else who has the misfortune to find themselves in the same situation?

I suppose I have, perhaps.

First, try not to have a stroke. It's most definitely not fun. There's lots you can do to avoid it. Lose weight. Take exercise. Keep the blood pressure down, and if the weight-loss and the exercise don't work, demand and take medication. It's a rough guide. I offer this with no official medical approval whatsoever, and disclaim any responsibility, but top-end blood pressure should be your age + 100, and below 90 at the bottom level. I'm sorry, but despite the danger of turning people into a nation of hypochondriacs, if you're over 45, buy a blood-pressure monitor from Boots or wherever, and use it.

That bit of advice you'd probably get from any competent GP, though the best of them might worry about producing people who think they're ill when they're not. There is a body of medical opinion – well, actually, two doctors who've talked to me off the record – who think that our blood pressure swings up and down fairly wildly throughout the day, without much visible harm.

The second conclusion is more tricky. I hesitate to offer it because I'm trying to reduce tension in my life, not add to it, and I don't want to get into more trouble and present myself as a crank. I don't make a habit of talking to trees, am in touch with the sides of me that I want to talk to and have no knowledge of alternative medicine, other than an interest in acupuncture. Conventional medicine is making huge advances, perhaps more so than ever in the history of humanity. Someone very close to me has had an operation with key-hole surgery that even five years ago would have required the patient to spend a fortnight in hospital; instead, within a fortnight, they were walking (slowly) without crutches. Yet the more important the doctor becomes, and the more important the impenetrable layers of knowledge of scientific medicine, the more the patient is relegated to a wholly subsidiary position.

Yet again I remember my father.

Always listen to the patient, he said, and he both meant and did it. The patient may know nothing about medical science, but he or she is in very intimate communication with their own body. I've had a very nasty, aggressive cancer. I knew something serious was wrong, or my body told me, but twice over, with a year between them, the battery of tests persuaded a top, brilliant consultant to say ... no. Just not convinced. Hang around a bit. Let's see what happens.

Of course, I ignored my own advice. Cancer OK, my body told me. I touch wood as I say it. Heart ... my body is telling me this isn't right. So I see another top, brilliant consultant. A cardiologist this time. On the day of the examination, and for the only 48 hours in its life that it has worn a portable recording monitor, my heart behaves perfectly. *Yet I know it's not right!* What should I have done? Played merry hell the next time my heart went walkabout. Demanded to see someone, anyone. I am now on simple medication, and for the vast majority of time, my heartbeat is as regular as Big Ben.

All this could have been done beforehand. Before I suffered my stroke. But I was too happy at being told I was well, too fearful of making a fuss. I'm sure the patient gets it wrong more often than the doctor or the consultant. I'm sure that some people come to define themselves by their illness, real or imagined. Yet I'm also sure that as a science and tests take over medicine more and more, we lose more and more respect for the mere patient's intuitive understanding of their own body. The temptation must be to see medicine not just as more of a science, but more of an *exact* science. I wonder if this doesn't mean that doctors are frightened of making a move before a conclusive test result comes through, even though there may never be a conclusive test result. I wonder if a modern doctor can ever back a hunch without feeling a lawyer breathing down his or her neck.

Third, if I had known then what I know now, I'd have been even more horrified that I was given no drive or encouragement to recover, provided with virtually no information about what I had suffered and, while wrapped round with the most immense kindness, left to rot. There was no sense of urgency, no drive. Kindness is not enough. Energy is also needed.

Fourth, I learnt a lot about relatives and friends. I learnt that they need to know not to judge what's going on inside one's head by the fact that some of the normal means of communication – speech, hand gestures, eyes – are screwed up and not working properly. They need to assume that the brain is fine unless there is real evidence that the contrary is true. Even more important is the boost family and friends give to the patient. I don't know what would have happened to me if my family hadn't rallied round, but it wouldn't have been good. In those crucial early days, the family are the emotional Zimmer frame, the prop on which you lean and learn to be yourself again. Your family and friends are a reminder of what used to be, a reason for trying to get better.

Fifth, I learnt what a crucial influence an employer can be. If they play it right, they provide motivation that persuades the patient that it is worth getting better. I am, by the way, very grateful to my employer.

The Diary of a Stroke

So there I was. I was home, out of the mausoleum at last and facing a very uncertain future. That uncertainty affects many stroke victims badly, adding to their frustration and fear, and making them very difficult to live with.

What, I can hear my family say as they read this: *more* difficult to deal with? As it is, whilst a stroke does not often change a person's personality, it can take the restraints off parts of their personality that have always been there but they have tried to repress. Angry people often become angrier after a stroke.

Well, I was angry and going to stay that way. But I was also going to get better. I just needed to work out a way of doing it.

Regeneration, Examination
and Cure

Week 2 and After

The next two or three weeks are crucial, and the days merge into so much of a similar pattern that they cannot be distinguished from each other.

The illness itself and the stay in hospital have created an adrenalin rush. Now I'm at home, in comfortable surroundings, I'm frightened that I will slip into lethargy, a cotton wool world where no one demands much of me and I demand little of myself. I've an excuse for doing nothing, for wandering around looking pale and interesting. I really need a Sergeant Major shouting at me all day long. I work out a programme.

The pattern of the day consists of three essential parts. There is the routine I work out with my wife, which dominates my whole attention. There are visits to medical authorities, which start at the end of the first week at home. And there are those who come to visit me.

The routine is a killer. I mustn't allow myself to stay in bed, must discipline myself to be out of bed by 8.00 am. This is almost the hardest part of it all. It's so easy to stay in bed! It's warm and comfortable. Under the duvet is my own little world where, if I'm that stupid, I can fool myself into believing that everything is all right, it's just another Sunday at the end of a busy week, the one day in the week where I don't have to get up. One of the few things that hasn't changed in the past few days is lying down in bed. In that position my inability to write, to walk straight, to speak properly and so on are invisible. Lying in bed I'm me, as I've always been me, not the new disabled version.

I divide the day up into two-hour stints. First, there are the tennis balls. Or, rather the five or six tennis balls, that number being needed because of my capacity to lose them. The idea is to bounce the tennis ball off a wall or on the floor and catch it. In my case, I choose to do this with my left hand and arm, as they are the worst affected. My father-in-law couldn't stand up, so he had to do this from a bed, bouncing the ball off a wall. This required my mother-in-law to chase the missed balls, but I can stand up. If I try to throw the ball on to the floor, I can't control the force, with the result that some balls bounce up and hit the ceiling, and others just land with a limp thump on the floor. The solution is to find the right ball that, if it's just dropped on to a hard floor, will bounce up high enough to be caught. The target is to catch the ball 2,000 times a day. There's no magic in the number. It's simply the one my father-in-law latched on to. It is, however, an extraordinarily high number when one comes down to actually trying to do it.

2,000 balls take a long time.

Worse, the ball has a mind of its own, and will, for no obvious reason, sometimes bounce sideways. I find it impossible to catch virtually any of the balls when I start. I drop the ball, watch it bounce but more often than not, I fail to catch it and just succeed in knocking it to one side. Dropped catches don't count. It then goes on a freelance bounce round the kitchen, where I have to chase it and pin it down.

As Sod's Law is the only universal legislation, the ball is guaranteed to end up under the kitchen table, behind chairs or anywhere other than where it is easy to get to. As bending down is a major exercise, the exercise rapidly becomes a farce. At my first ten attempts. I catch the ball, once, badly, and that is a pure fluke. The rest of the time I'm skittling around trying to track down the elusive ball. I make my first compromise. I will *try* to catch it 2,000 times. But if I fail, that will still count as a try, and when I reach 2,000, I can stop.

I try to get the dog to retrieve the balls. Not a great idea. First of all, he hasn't got a clue as to what he's meant to do. Then some vague idea enters what passes for a dog's brain that, perhaps he's meant to get the ball. This offends some of his deepest principles. He's a stick dog. Balls are for … poodles. He quite likes me – I feed him sometimes, don't I? – so he compromises, picking up the ball, shaking it a few times, then runs out in the garden and drops it at the far end, after which he cocks his leg against a tree and goes back in, mission accomplished, tail wagging.

In fact, the 2,000 figure is impossible on that first day in anything like one session. It will take me over ten days before I can do it in one lump of time. 300 is the maximum I can manage in one session on that first day, and even at that I'm exhausted and dripping with sweat. It's taken me nearly 45 minutes, what with scrabbling around on the floor and my painfully slow retrieval time.

I crawl back upstairs, and sleep for two hours. So much for getting up.

Next is the handwriting. I've just got to start again and can't postpone the evil day. It's a good thing to do after the tennis balls, because I can do it sitting down. It's also on the same floor as the bedroom, so I don't have to go downstairs. The writing is crucial, both for my self-respect and my job. It simply has to come back. I find myself the A4 pad we got in hospital. I have lots of pens. I love pens, and because friends and family know this, it's always been a good present for me. I go through various choices. I'm dismayed by how alien the pens feel, sticking through my fist as if I have no real control over them. Holding a pen used to be the most natural thing in the world. The best one seems to be an expensive Parker roller ball. The grip is slightly fluted, it's not too fat and it sits a little more easily than the others.

I start with the date on the top line, like a small child doing his first school exercise. It's laughable. I can't do circles, or half circles. The loops under 'y' or 'g' I can't control at all, and most of the time they'll rip aside and puncture the top of the letter. My signature is also laughable, unrecognisable. Oddly, I'm not depressed by this, though I don't know why. I just feel determined. I've always been able to write. It's something I do. The rock fall of the stroke has buried the skill, but it's been a part of me for so long that I'm sure, really sure, deep down sure, that it's all still there. It just needs a massive slog of digging to unearth it.

I start a line. I'll fill it with my best stab at the letter 'a', until I've filled the line. I try not to look too hard at

1. An attempt to make notes from
a telephone call, one week after the stroke.

2. The first handwriting sheet that I kept,
about a week after the stroke.

I'm starting to despair.
Even a single page
seems to take hours.

[rows of handwriting practice strokes and letter forms]

Martin Stephen. Martin Stephen . Martin Stephen . Martin Stephen
Martin Stephen . Martin Stephen. Martin Stephen . Martin Stephen
Martin Stephen . Martin Ste
Martin Stephen . Martin Stephen
Martin Stephen . Martin Step
Martin Stephen . Martin St

At last! 14th October, and some
sign of returning normality. But
the signature is still surprising bad.

Martin Stephen Martin Stephen

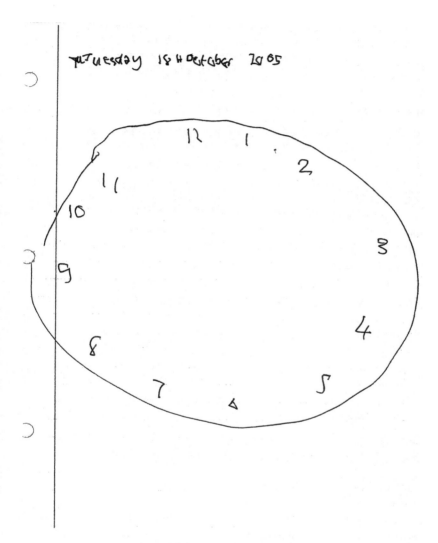

Tuesday 18 H October 2005

12 1 2
11
10
9   3
8   4
7   6   5

An exercise suggested by my GP.

135

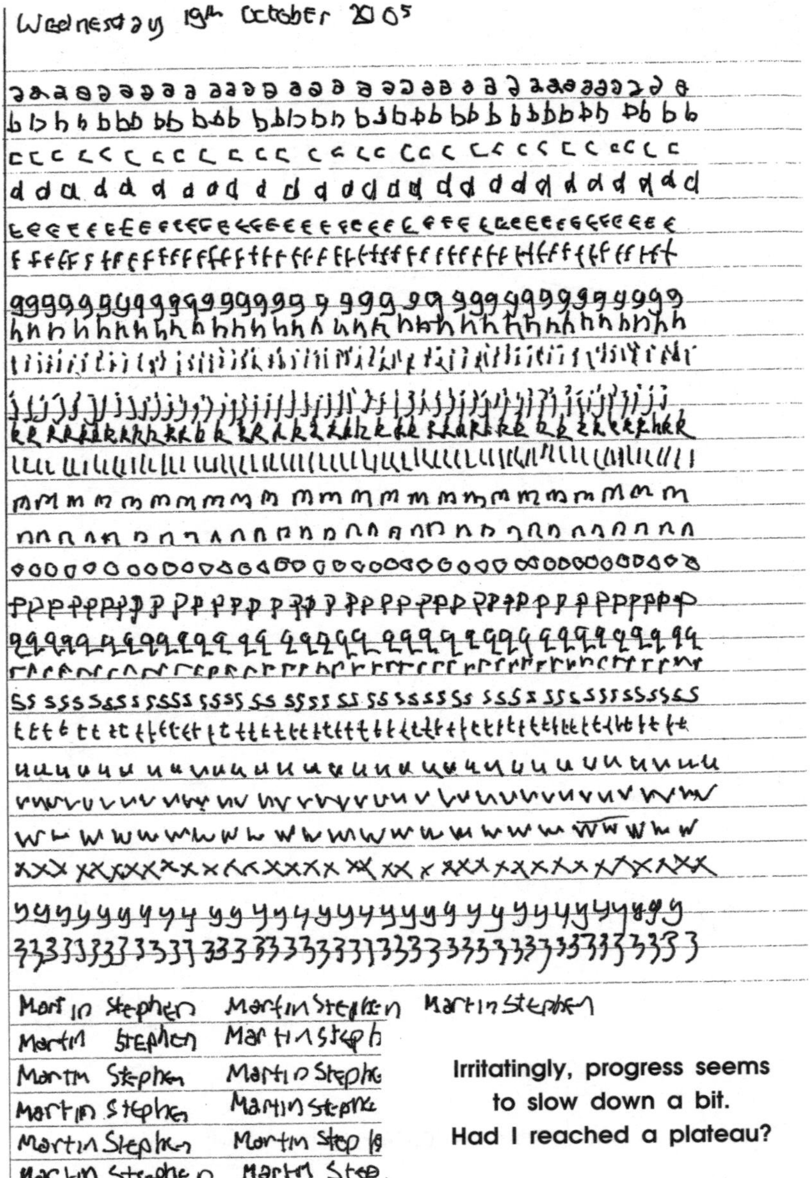

The Diary of a Stroke

Wednesday 19th October 2005

[Rows of repeated handwritten practice letters of the alphabet: a, b, c, d, e, f, g, h, i, j, k, l, m, n, o, p, q, r, s, t, u, v, w, x, y, 3]

Martin Stephen	Martin Stephen	Martin Stephen
Martin Stephen	Martin Steph	
Martin Stephen	Martin Stephe	**Irritatingly, progress seems**
Martin Stephen	Martin Stephe	**to slow down a bit.**
Martin Stephen	Martin Step l	**Had I reached a plateau?**
Martin Stephen	Martin Step.	

the result. Then I go on to 'b', and so on all the way through the alphabet. The 'b' looks remarkably similar to the 'a'. A large number of the letters look disarmingly similar. I'm amazed by how long the whole thing takes. I'm having to craft each letter, as if it were something made out of lead individually. After half an hour of laborious work, I'm not even half way through the alphabet. My arm aches. Why my arm, and not my hand? My head hurts, literally. It's a dull pain unlike any other headache I've had before. Is it eye strain? Or some new malign development inside my head? The comfort is the memory of the times I've had to get fit, for hockey, for coaching soccer or for white water canoeing. It's always the same. When you start to get fit again, you always throw up half-way along the first run. It's like the stitch in your side, you just have to run through it.

I finish the scrawling – I can't even keep some of the letters on a straight line – and try my signature again. I can recognise eight, nine of the letters, no more. I finish my self-imposed task with a huge sense of relief and put the pen down.

Later that night, I go back to the pad. I see these indecipherable squiggles, and my heart sinks. I screw up the paper, throw it away. I continue to do that for three, four, maybe five days. I keep the first sheet on the day that I persuade myself that some control is coming back. I do not try and write the date on the top. I decide the only reason to do so is to mark progress, and that if there isn't any, I will only depress myself.

That first sheet is reproduced here, as are some others, each a few days apart. The sheet with the clock (p. 135) marked '18th October' is the first time I dared date a page, though I had been keeping them and not screwing them up for some days. The remarkable change in the quality of my writing must therefore have taken a fortnight from my stroke to that date. The final sheet (see p. 156) is my handwriting as it now is, very little different from what it had always been.

The hieroglyphics are my attempt to write down a phone message.

The lawn still has stripes on it from being mowed, even though the grass has stopped growing. This is a town house, overlooked by neighbours, but by urban standards very private. I decide to walk up and down each stripe of grass, keeping within its bounds. There are eleven stripes. I have to be firm with myself. If my foot so much as strays over to the next stripe, I must go back to the start again. As with so much early on, progress is laughable. I've already bruised my shoulder walking into the door jamb on several occasions. It takes me six attempts to get to the end of the first stripe, even at my painfully slow place. I'm still walking like an old man, feet splayed out like a duck.

I decide if I'm going to survive I can get away with walking up the first stripe and down the second, and so on to the eleventh, rather than up and down each one. As it's an odd number I won't be walking up or down the same one in the same direction. It'll change every time I do the round of the eleven stripes. That's my justification for making it easier for myself.

The dog can't understand why its owner is walking funereally up and down the lawn. He lies down, eyeing me carefully to see if anything at all interesting is going to happen. It doesn't. Never mind him. Nothing interesting is happening to me. The tennis balls were infuriating. The writing was depressing. The lawn is, at least, different. It's mind-blowingly boring. The hero of the novels I write, one Henry Gresham, invents sonnets in his head when he gets truly bored, during the Spanish Armada or on the Irish campaign preceding the Earl of Essex's rebellion in 1601. The rhyme scheme and metre are a nightmare. I try it. And fail. I'm just not a poet. Instead, I start talking to the garden birds. They are unimpressed.

I finish my assault course. It's completely flat, contains no obstacles other than those in my mind. As I am now, it is more challenging than all the assault courses I went on as a young 'officer' in the Combined Cadet Force.

I persuade myself not to go back to bed.

Lunch time. I try to put a plate down on the table, and end up banging it down like a broken flying saucer hitting the ground. Mercifully, it does not break. I've still not boiled a kettle. This is silly. I was fool enough to do a wet shave and stand in a shower flying in the face of all reason. I might as well try to conquer the kettle routine, I kill the kettle by means of jamming the spout into the tap end and holding it there until it spills out water. The kettle hisses and sizzles on the Aga, and comes to the boil. I lob a tea bag into a mug. It misses. I try again. This time the tea bag goes inside the mug. I pick the kettle up, and manage to put half the water on to the Aga and half in to the mug. The problem is that my hand is swinging backwards and forwards. Again, as I did with the plate, I intend to put the kettle down but find that I have banged it hard back down on the Aga. I manage to take out the tea bag, and put it in the compost box. Half the milk goes over the Aga, half in to the mug. There seems to be a pattern here, I think. In fact, the half mug is a blessing. It doesn't spill when that strange, swooping movement cuts in. It's actually the same movement that swept the glasses into the waiter's lap at the conference hotel all those days ago. I can put a hand on the mug. When I get it near my lips that bit is fine. It's in between that's difficult. I bang the mug, hard, into my front teeth. They survive.

When I finish lunch, I walk out of the kitchen door. Except I don't walk out of the door. I walk into the side of the door frame, banging my shoulder. It hurts; there is already a huge black bruise there from other strange encounters and I feel unreasonably angry.

Back to work. It's got to be the tennis balls, though my heart sinks at the prospect. It's no longer a tennis ball, at least inside my own head. It's That Bloody Thing. The Bloody Thing that keeps bouncing away. I can see that the Tennis Ball Bouncing (when I see it in my head it is always in Capital Letters) is going to be the *bête noire* of my rehab programme. I manage another 300 attempted bounces, the success rate not much different from the morning. I resist the temptation, just, to bounce the occasional ball off the dog's head, simply so that another creature in the house can have something to get annoyed about.

My eldest son is living at home between flats. He is desperately concerned about my health, and he appoints himself as Chief Commissar of the Food Police. My every

140

mouthful is watched, stern words spoken if so much as a single e-number passes my lips. Vast quantities of fruit are pulped in the industrial-size machine he has bought to produce home-made smoothies. Well, I suppose I've been ordering him around for 30 years. It's only fair that he has his turn.

My GP comes round. You can spot he's a saint, by the very rare combination of the title 'GP' with the two words 'come round'. GP's don't come round any more, unless they are very special ones like this man. He smiles at me, comes in, and tries not to make it clear that he's watching me walk, listening to me talk. The medical officer in *Star Trek* has a wonderful machine, called a tricorder, that he passes over the body and which instantly tells him everything that's wrong. My GP doesn't need a machine. He just has his eyes, and he uses them. For the first time, the NHS comes up trumps. The GP is hugely, hugely encouraging. He emanates a belief that I can and will get better, and so becomes the first person with a medical qualification to show actual faith in me. He also treats me like an adult, and explains simply and clearly what a stroke is, how it happens, what it means. *This is the first time I have been given any real information by a medic about what has happened to me.* He does not tell me whether I will recover or not; he seems to be saying, 'that's up to you'.

Suddenly, I'm empowered, given a new lease of life. He talks to me calmly, practically, neither blinding me with science nor using bland medical buzzwords. He makes suggestions to add to my rehab programme. One of them is music to my ears.

Shoot 'em up computer games will be wonderful for hand-eye co-ordination, he tells me.

I love shoot 'em up computer games. I actually managed to blow up the Death Star in the first *Star Wars* game. Does this mean that at least one part of my programme might actually be *fun*? This is a new thought, and it is wonderfully pleasing. Ever so gently, the GP maps some of the problems I will face. He announces his intention to explore physio for me, and to find whatever rehab programmes might help. Somehow, he manages not to make them sound threatening. When he leaves, I feel as if I've passed my first test. On thinking about it, I suspect this is exactly what he intended me to feel.

Keep it professional, we are always told. Personal feelings cloud the judgement. Don't get personally involved in your job. My GP has just given me the first real boost I've received from the medical profession because he's broken all these rules. He's talked to me personally, as a human being. He's suggested to me that my recovery really matters to him, not just as a doctor but as a fellow member of the human race. The difference it's made to my state of mind is phenomenal. Later, much later, I realise why that visit was such a turning point. My GP did not just look at me and listen to me but said, in effect, that he backed me in the battle to make myself better.

I think that until his visit I only knew that I was fighting this dreadful thing that had happened to me because fighting was all I could do. After he visited, my mind-set changed subtly. I was no longer fighting for fighting's sake. I was fighting to make a complete recovery.

Now I believed I could do it. A doctor appeared to believe I could do it, and now I really believed, rather than just hoping, that I could.

I know something has changed, because when I reach 300 bounces of The Bloody Thing I feel a surge of confidence, and vow to do 100 more. I make it, just. Or do I miss out on the last 10? I don't care. I'm exhausted, but this is my first day on my own, and I know, I just know, that I've climbed a mountain simply by keeping going.

I pack it all in then, and wait for my wife to come home so that I can babble – or slur – inanities to her, pathetic little details of the pathetic little mountains I've climbed. She has her own challenges, her own worries and her own concerns. She listens to my petty account of the day as if it is the most important thing in life. I felt rather like the late Victorian wife who has nothing to do all day except wait for her husband to come home, and then bores him with the astounding revelation that she's actually done nothing all day.

My wife has been shopping. She has bought a child's toy and made it up. It is a present. It is a wiggly wire, connected through a transformer to a mains-powered buzzer, and a metal loop. You have to follow the wiggly wire with the loop; if the loop touches the wire, a buzzer goes off; it sounds like those gadgets in Germanic cars that get cross when you leave the lights on or the keys in the lock. I might as well jam the loop of wire into the National Grid for all my capacity to control its movements. The buzzer drives me round the bend.

'I thought you were bored,' she says innocently. I glare at her, lose concentration and the buzzer goes off again.

I assert my moral rights when it comes to one of the other toys she's bought. Stringing beads. There are limits. I refuse to string beads. I've kept the box, as a reminder of how bad times can be.

There's one thing I've forgotten to say. My wife's employer has a brother who is a leading medic. He provides a list of the best cardiologists and stroke specialists in the UK. I have private medical health insurance. The brother makes the first contact, and when he has cleared the way, my wife rings up. The cardiologist agrees to see me.

Not for a single moment do I consider refusing the appointment. I can't. My family want me alive, and not just because of my earning potential. I've no desire to be disabled, and even less of a desire to suffer another stroke.

Yet supposing I didn't have private medical insurance? Supposing my own father hadn't been a rather wise GP? Supposing my father-in-law hadn't had a serious stroke? Supposing we didn't move in circles where the names of the 'best' cardiologists are known?

I suspect I'd have been forgotten, as I was forgotten in my hospital bed.

And that's wrong. Every which way I turn, it's wrong. Surely the best medical care is a right, not a privilege, for every member of an advanced society? How about the people who don't have private medical insurance?

All my deep moral reservations count for nothing when I come to deciding what to do, of course. Does the drowning man ask the passing lifebelt whether it has been provided free of charge by the Government, or was included in the first class ticket? I want to get better, and I'll take any support that's on offer. At the moment I just don't want to drown, and it's the floating, rather than who keeps me buoyant that seems to matter most. The pangs of moral conscience will come later, a luxury after the event.

I make an appointment for Friday. That's good. Friday can now become a target. How much can I do to make myself better by Friday?

I'm in bed by nine o'clock. Exhausted. The body takes a bashing from something like a stroke, and apart from the obvious symptoms, I simply do not have the reserves of energy I'm used to. Instead of running on battery power when I run out of steam, it's as if I'm running on that battery from the first moment in the morning. I'm asleep in ten minutes, but before I slip away my mind returns to my father, who for obvious reasons has been more in my thoughts these past few days than almost at any time since his death over 25 years ago. The thoughts are sparked by the visit of my GP.

Like everyone else I'd become accustomed to having to wait a week for an appointment with the popular GP in the practice, and viewed asking for a home visit or ringing and asking to speak to my GP as a fond fantasy. My present GP is the exception to that rule, but memories that had lain hidden for years came flooding back. My father had done a morning and an evening surgery, and home visits after both, sometimes as many as twenty. Why do I remember? I used to drive him sometimes, when I was a student at home in the vacation, simply to ease the load on him. I think occasionally I had also come with him in the car, just for company. I remember his frustration at people who didn't display their house numbers prominently, and that he fitted what was, in effect, a small searchlight to his car so that he could pick out the house numbers at night.

Tuesday dawns and I manage to dawn with it. The urge to stay in bed, to doze and to drift, is huge, bigger and more pressing than even yesterday. Some deeply-buried survival instinct tells me that this is a crucial battle with my own mind and body. Battered as they are, they want the easy way out. I mustn't let them have their way.

If I give in I give up. As with so many things – giving up smoking, getting fit again – the first few days are the worst. There is both a credibility and a pain barrier to overcome. That gremlin in my brain whispers at me all the time. Does he mean it? Is he going to keep at it? Or can we grind him down, say the siren rebel voices in my mind. After a couple of days they will give in and let me get on, but on this, the second day, I don't know that. The opposition, those creatures in my head who just want me to sit back and give in, are very loud again all of a sudden.

I have a new toy today. It's a cork. I'm worried about my slurred speech. I'm hammering the hand-eye co-ordination, the walking, the writing, but I'm doing nothing for the speech, though it is getting better. Speech is delivered by the tongue and the lips. How to make them work harder? If you put a normal, wine-bottle sized cork in your mouth, jam it between your upper and lower front teeth, and try to speak with normal lip and tongue movements, you sound something like I did after the stroke. To produce normal speech, you have to work the lips and the mouth far harder, really exaggerate their

146

movements. I decide to read out loud, with a cork between my teeth, for at least an hour a day.

What to read? Well, my eyes and print are still not on the best of terms. Basically, I can't read for more than a few minutes before my eyes go walkabout. I suddenly realise I have another exercise to add to the task list.

Reading.

Now there's a thing.

My first absolutely crystal-clear memory, as distinct from a vague impression, is of standing in the kitchen in my childhood home and asking my mother, who was by the rather harsh stainless steel sink, what year it was. I was five years old at the time. I know this because my mother answered that it was 1955. I remember feeling that in some strange way this was very profound. I was five. It was 1955. My fascination with this coincidence argues for a very early interest in, and sympathy with, numbers that must have somehow dried up pretty quickly afterwards, if my problems with maths at school are anything to go by.

But at the edge of my memory, though still crystal-clear and certain, is another thing. I was holding a book, in my left hand, and sucking the left corner of its cover. We didn't have paperbacks in our house. In retrospect this was a good thing, as if the book hadn't been a hardback – though cheap, tatty and already very soiled – perhaps I might have died of paper poisoning. The book was Robert Louis Stevenson's *Treasure Island*. Heaven knows how I had found it. I suspect it confirms my belief that the only imperative programmed in to me from birth was finding something to read. And as I've said that in a manuscript I'm increasingly beginning to think no one will ever read, thank you to Mrs Pettigrew who provided me with the technical means of doing so, and Mrs Mildred Kirk-Smith for making me enjoy it. Was it Mildred who gave 'Treasure Island' to me at the ripe old age of five? I wouldn't have put it past her. Either way, I've been addicted to reading for as long as I can remember. I like computer games, in a guilty sort of way but they're no contest. Reading? Now that was an addiction, pure and simple. Getting the skill to read back in place, now that is a drive to beat all drives.

But where to start for my two hours a day of reading out loud? Well, I think I know two or three poems by Andrew Marvell, the metaphysical poet, off by heart. Why not use him for both my reading and my speech rehab.? Surely my passion for his poetry will help push my reading and my speaking through the pain barrier? It does. I've been quoting 'To His Coy Mistress' wrongly for 20 years, I discover, as I consult the original for the first time in as many years. I feel a complete fool, reading out loud the work of a long dead poet, to an empty room.

To his Coy Mistress
by Andrew Marvell

Had we but world enough, and time,
This coyness, lady, were no crime.
We would sit down and think which way
To walk, and pass our long love's day;
Thou by the Indian Ganges' side

148

Shouldst rubies find; I by the tide
Of Humber would complain. I would
Love you ten years before the Flood;
And you should, if you please, refuse
Till the conversion of the Jews.
My vegetable love should grow
Vaster than empires, and more slow.
An hundred years should go to praise
Thine eyes, and on thy forehead gaze;
Two hundred to adore each breast,
But thirty thousand to the rest;
An age at least to every part,
And the last age should show your heart.
For, lady, you deserve this state,
Nor would I love at lower rate.

But at my back I always hear
Time's winged chariot hurrying near;
And yonder all before us lie
Deserts of vast eternity.
Thy beauty shall no more be found,
Nor, in thy marble vault, shall sound
My echoing song; then worms shall try
That long preserv'd virginity,
And your quaint honour turn to dust,
And into ashes all my lust.
The grave's a fine and private place,
But none I think do there embrace.

Now therefore, while the youthful hue
Sits on thy skin like morning dew,

The Diary of a Stroke

And while thy willing soul transpires
At every pore with instant fires,
Now let us sport us while we may;
And now, like am'rous birds of prey,
Rather at once our time devour,
Than languish in his slow-chapp'd power.
Let us roll all our strength, and all
Our sweetness, up into one ball;
And tear our pleasures with rough strife
Thorough the iron gates of life.
Thus, though we cannot make our sun
Stand still, yet we will make him run.

I've been saying for years 'But always at my back I hear, Time's winged chariot hurrying near.' The actual line is, 'But at my back I always hear...'

The fun's over.

Now I have to do all the other things. The damned tennis ball, the lawn, the loop and the buzzer ... I'm saved by my wife, just as I'm about to start screaming and frothing at the mouth. She brings home three computer games, two 'Star Wars' and one about flying an F15 jet.

I fly the jet in its gloriously complicated and lifelike simulation. Throttle boosters need to be placed in the 5/8 position while flap angle is adjusted accordingly and the snag boosting widget is calibrated against Venus being in the ascendant in Mars. Or something. Simple, really. If this simulation is anything like the real thing, I'm amazed anyone ever flies. I never even reach the stage of dog-fighting the whole time I play the game. I simply learn to go direct to the training section, where you can land the plane as someone has already taken it up in to the air. This is a good thing, as I have no doubt that my ability to get the aircraft into the air would be as disastrous as my ability (or non-ability) to land it. It's the hand problem again. My hand swoops the plane from left to right, up and down, in a manner that would squash any real pilot flat. Time after time I hopelessly miss the runway or just crash on to it.

This really, really isn't working. I'm appalled at my inability to control the joystick. The plane swings sickeningly left and right again, turns on its head. I try again. It must be the twentieth time. The runway can just be seen in the distance. I swing so wildly to left and right that frequently I lose sight of the runway. It seems almost impossible to get it back within sight. I take a perverse pleasure in nose-diving the plane into the ground. The sound effects are gratifying.

I start the habit of doing a report card for each day, in my mind, of course.

Testing Testing

Tuesday

Another week on. It's all getting a little better, but some bits are responding better than others. The writing is bad, very bad. My vision seems to have come back to normal in terms of seeing one, two, three or four versions of one single object, but it's also changed. I now need something for reading, as I'm squinting at the printed word.

The walking is definitely getting better too. For the first time today I walked down the stairs, instead of going down them on my bottom. I'd vowed I'd only go down that way for one day, before realising that my body simply couldn't do it any other way.

And my speech? Difficult to say, but my wife says that it's back to normal half the time, slightly slurred the rest. Capacity to pour and hold a cup of tea? Better, but still bad. Doorways hopeless. Sitting down and staying in control for the vital last bit? Forget it. And everything in my hand goes bang when it touches a hard surface.

Wednesday

Easier to get up this morning, a bit. Some sort of routine is being established. There's something new for today, thank God. I'm starting to think that boredom is the biggest enemy to recovery. The new thing is the realisation that the first edit of my next novel arrived just before I went off for the conference.

I love writing my novels. They're historical crime thrillers set in the late 16th and early 17th centuries, and came after a string of books on English literature and modern naval history. The period fascinates me, with its huge contrasts between the medieval and the modern world, and the fact that it contains four or five of the greatest unsolved whodunits in history, including the Spanish Armada, the failure of the Earl of Essex's rebellion against Elizabeth I in 1601, the peaceful accession of James I, the Gunpowder Plot and who wrote Shakespeare's plays. This is my fourth novel, and it is tricky because, unlike the others, the action is set over a number of years. The first edit is the crucial phase in the writing of a novel. The author writes what he or she thinks is the best stab at their work. The editor then reads it, and sends back suggestions for change. It's an extraordinary job, being an editor. You have to tune into the whole being of the author, and 'edit' what they've written so that you highlight what they want to say and mean. You act, in effect, like an amplifier to the author's original noise.

Editors are usually blessed with high intelligence, and a degree that puts their author's qualifications to shame. They have names like Tara or Annabelle, and, rather irritatingly, look about eighteen years old. They exude competence, and magnificent patience with the author. The temptation to change the novel to what the editor would have written, had they been the author, must be huge.

I happen to like and respect my editor. I was looking forward, genuinely, to the forthcoming battle, in which I would agree to some of her suggestions, disagree forcibly with (a few) others (and then give in with bad grace a bit later), and try to amalgamate all her suggestions in to my original text. As it is, the edit gives me a real opportunity. Two real opportunities, as I think about it.

First, if a thinking bit of my brain has died because of the stroke, this will show it. This is something that has worried at me ever since the immediate aftermath of the stroke. How would I know if crucial brain cells had been burnt out? Does a person who's become less intelligent, lost real brain power, know it? Editing a novel is actually very demanding on the brain, not because of vast philosophical edifices of thought that have to be erected and maintained – my novels aren't like that; they're just meant to be fun – but because my plotting is very complex. I try to keep the plot and the characters balanced, and it is a real intellectual juggling act.

Secondly, all my writing and editing is done on computer. For my handwriting I'm bashing out meaningless letters. Yet my typing and keyboard skills are, if anything, worse than my handwriting. Flying an F15 to an early grave, I notice I can't even centre the mouse on an icon, let alone double click fast enough to make it work. I can only do a single click. But now I've got the chance, or rather the excuse, to hammer away at my keyboard and typing skills whilst doing something useful, and something I actually enjoy. It's got to be better than the treadmill of the tennis ball, the walk up and down the lawn, the Victorian copy book writing. So much so that I can bribe myself with the editing and promise myself it as a reward when yet another treadmill exercise is completed.

The Next Week

Today I collapse. Not physically. Mentally. I go to bed for two, three hours, give up, give in. When my wife comes home, I pretend it hasn't happened. After two hours with her, it is as if it hadn't.

Friday, Saturday, Sunday, Monday. The weekend is better, my wife and some of my family at home, bringing a sense of normality. I manage to keep up the regime, albeit with fewer hours spent on each task so that I can talk to people. We go to the local farmers' market on Saturday. I feel immensely pleased with myself despite the fact that I'm driven to a car parking space a few yards from the market. I walk there, actually walk through the tiny market. It feels good. Then, out of nowhere, a wave of exhaustion hits me. I retreat to the entrance, and sit on a traffic bollard.

I'm bum on bollard when a colleague from work greets me.

'Hello', I say. Yes, I'm making a splendid, miraculous recovery. Isn't it great? Now please go away before I collapse and fall off this bollard. Thank you.

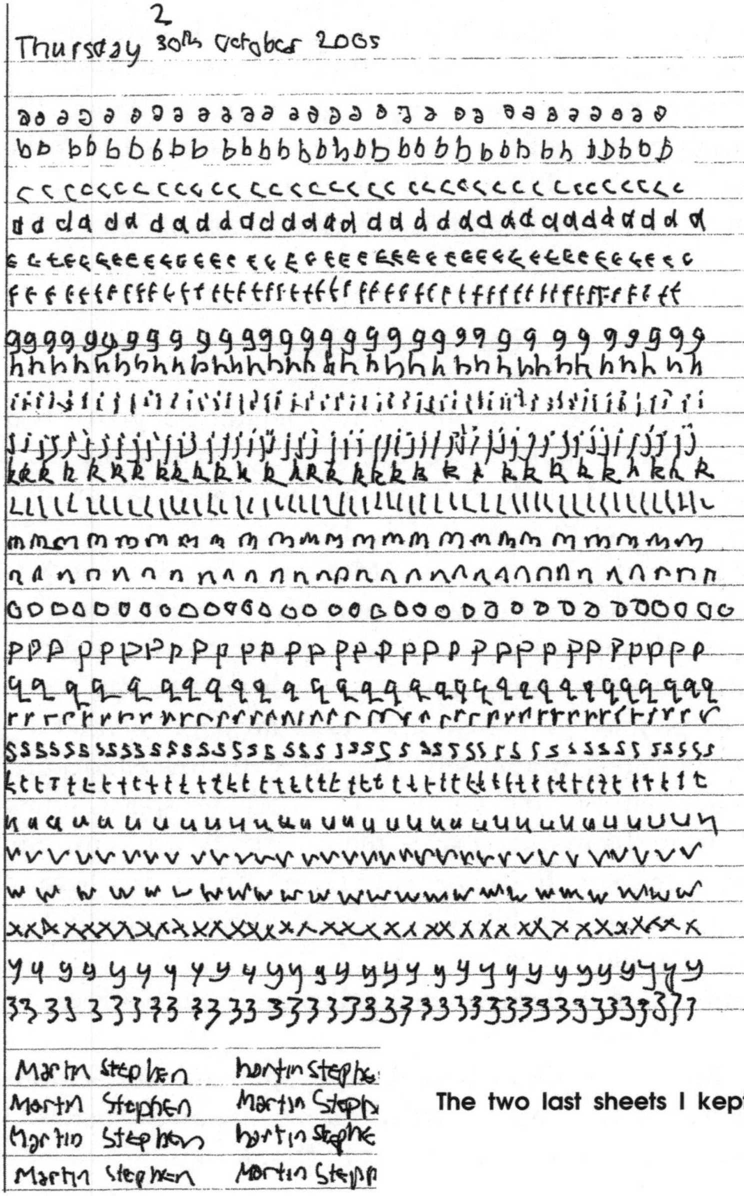

Thursday 30th October 2005

(rows of repeated handwriting-practice letters: a, b, c, d, e, f, g, h, i, j, k, l, m, n, o, p, q, r, s, t, u, v, w, x, y, z)

Martin Stephen   Martin Stephe
Martin Stephen   Martin Steph
Martin Stephen   Martin Stephe
Martin Stephen   Martin Stephn

The two last sheets I kept.

156

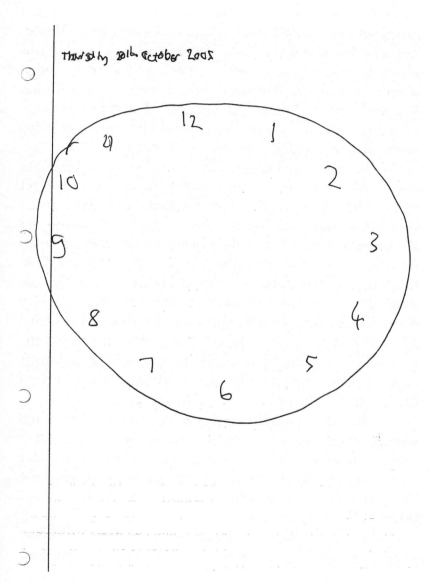

Thursday 20th October 2005

The Diary of a Stroke

Monday comes, and I'm on something of a roll. The only problem is that the computer games are so much more fun than anything else so that I'm spending too much time on them to the exclusion of the other exercises. The first week has been like pushing at a rock fall. Now, all of a sudden, things are happening. The rocks move when I push them. There's daylight ahead, and fresh air. My sense of excitement is tangible. The letters I form with my hand are becoming recognisable, and my hand aches just that much less after each session.

On Tuesday I land an F15. OK, alarm noises keep going off, it's skewed round on the virtual runway and I don't know what to do when I have landed, but I did it, with the plane (just about) in one (computer) piece. On Wednesday, after an hour of slavishly copying the alphabet, I reach the end, 'z'. And then, as a treat, I allow myself to write my own signature. I do it tiredly, resignedly. The better I get, the more I wonder if these exercises are any good ... and hey. That signature looks good, by which I mean it looks vaguely normal. I look at it again. It's the real thing. It will do. Immediately I write another signature. Wobbly. Distinctly wobbly. Never mind. Now I know I can do it, I will do it.

On Thursday, I go down again. A wave of depression sweeps over me. Improvements in my walking, writing and so on have become minimal again. I start to wonder how I will ever be able to cope with twelve hour working days, if, after two hours trying to catch a ball, I am overwhelmed by exhaustion.

I'm saved by Radio 4's *Today* programme. Not many people can say that. I appear on radio and TV every now and again. The *Today* programme have rung me to ask if I will appear in the 8.50 am slot next Saturday, to join in a discussion as to whether an Old Etonian could ever be elected again as Prime Minister. The programme don't know I've had a stroke. Very few people do, actually.

I start to think. If I can fool however many million people listen to Saturday's *Today* programme that I'm normal, maybe I'll believe it myself. I get excited at the challenge and the high stakes. If I get it wrong and do the programme badly, I'll believe something irreversible has happened to me. But the adrenalin rush is lifting me out of my depression. Some colour has been injected into my black and white world. It's not so much that I have something to look forward to, more that I have something to prepare for. It's a game, really, with stakes rather higher than crashing an imaginary F15. I change my training schedule and concentrate entirely on speaking. Will I slur my words? Will I stammer? Will my mind go blank, and will I find myself drying up on air?

I take a taxi to the studio, get there very early. You sign in, and an assistant takes you through a newsroom, open-plan desks littered with newspapers and memos. You are shown into a glass-walled room next door to, but separated from, the actual studio, which has a red light over the door when a live broadcast is taking place. The wall opposite the entrance to the glass room has a black and white photo-montage of past and present presenters of the programme. No pictures of their guests, I notice.

There's a coffee machine in the room with thin, bendy plastic cups, some newspapers on a chipped table and upholstered chairs that have seen better days. On a

159

cupboard opposite the coffee machine are some croissants and pastries, which guests have been eating. Discarded cling film litters the top. And not only guests have been having a go at the food. A man, 45 years old or so, wearing a BBC badge, sweeps in, grunts at me, and starts to pick over the tray. He takes a pastry, stuffs a large portion into his mouth and leaves, the remainder clutched in his paw and trailing crumbs. The man who will be appearing before me arrives ten minutes after I do. He is a famous author. I grit my teeth. Every time I come and do this programme there is a ruddy author on it, free to plug his books. All I ever get to do is to talk about education. I am very, very jealous, and made even more cross by the fact that the successful author, who is actually a far better writer than I will ever be, is also utterly charming – so I am even denied the solace of hating him.

You are left alone in the glass room in the middle of a strangely empty newsroom until they want you. At that moment a production assistant ushers you in to the studio, where the presenters (two of them on the *Today* programme) sit on one side of a circular table, wearing earphones. I am still moving very slowly, and it takes me an age to get out of a chair. I have to hold a half cup of coffee with one hand. I usually take a pen into the studio with me, to jot down thoughts as to what I might say as the discussion develops. Fat chance of that. I can't write properly. It'll have to be memory. I daren't take a cup of coffee or water in, in case I spray it round the studio.

Critically, I'm walking more slowly than anyone they've had in the studio, I suspect. If I wait for the production assistant to come in to the glass room and invite me through, it'll take me until next week's broadcast to get inside the studio. I sit right by the door, eyes on the studio door. I'll start to stand up as soon as it opens, start to walk towards the production assistant, meet her half-way. It could go seriously wrong. She could be coming out of the studio and not coming to invite me in, which would be embarrassing. I'm lucky; it is me she wants. I make it into the studio and sit down.

The presenters nod, smile, are charming. I'm not a politician. The discussion starts. I go into complete, total focus. I become a brain, a pair of ears and a mouth. My eyes stay open, but I am seeing nothing, because I'm concentrating so hard on listening and responding. It's as if the room has been plunged into darkness, and the only thing I can see is the microphone in front of me.

My brain, therefore, me, feels under pressure. I'm having to work incredibly hard not to sound like someone on helium, and to speak at a normal 33⅓ rpm, not 78 rpm. But it's working! I can feel it! A huge sense of exhilaration starts to sweep through me. It's not brilliant, my contribution, but it's clear, has a core of sense to it and does respond to the ebb and flow of the discussion. I'm sure I'm thinking no less quickly on my feet than before in these situations, the ideas and the thoughts clicking into place and producing words. And, wonderfully, I'm not stammering.

The discussion is over. I feel a massive, overwhelming sense of relief. I've been hiding from the fact that, just as I can't really do my job without being able to write and to type, neither can I do it without appearing in

161

front of large numbers of people. It's what Heads do. If I can appear before the Saturday audience of the *Today* programme and persuade them, it's business as normal.

There is one kick-back. Someone who knows I've had a stroke can't believe it's true, having heard me. If he's ill he should be in hospital: no business appearing on national radio. I'm severely criticised. You can't win.

Friday

A taxi takes my wife and myself to the consultant. He lives in Harley Street. Well he would, wouldn't he? The receptionist works for all the doctors in the building, and gives the impression of being slightly bored. She will tell the consultant's secretary I've arrived. She manages to make me feel ever so slightly that her even saying I've arrived is rather a favour. The waiting room is Edwardian, quite dark, big sofas and chairs, papers on a coffee table, free coffee – or, rather, free at the point of drinking – tea and water from machines that seem rather incongruous in the carefully furnished 'home' décor. There are two other patients there. One is an Arab lady, in her late 40s, shrouded. She is very overweight, and her eyes continually flick round the room. There is a strange expression on her face, a mixture of resignation and terror. This is not a lady who feels in control of anything.

I wish she had someone with her. I look at my wife, and realise how extraordinarily special it is to be as much in love with someone 38 years on as I was when I first fell in love with her, at first sight. The other patient is elderly, white, male. And definitely upper middle class. He is reading the paper intently, staring purposefully at it over *pince nez* spectacles. Unlike the Arab lady, he needs no help. Or perhaps would rather die before admitting to any need for help. I christen him The Major. Again, he is alone. Again, I realise how important my wife's presence there is to me. None of us say anything to each other. The silence is funereal. There is a loud gurgling noise, from the direction of the Major. I turn round, convinced The Major is in for some gargantuan problem with his plumbing. No such drama. It is the water cooler making the noise, not The Major's gut. He stares even more intently at his paper, and goes red.

We're marched in to see the consultant.

By this time I've become something of an expert on medical qualifications and the attendant hierarchy. At the bottom of the pile is the MD, or **Mere Doctor**. Their role is similar to that of the porter at the front entrance of the Ritz, namely to shepherd you, the patient, through the door and towards higher things. Higher things start with the NQC, or **Newly Qualified Consultant**. If he or she is lucky, over a period of years they will become CIA: **Consultant I've Arrived!** After this you aim for GCHQ: **Grand Consultant Highest Qualifications**. A very few them move on to the highest grade of the lot: GCSE, **Grand Consultant Superior and Extraordinaire**.

I sense immediately that this guy's a GCSE. We were told he was, and he is. It radiates forth. This is a very, very clever medic who knows more about how the heart operates than the heart itself. He sits behind a very large desk. In body language terms, the message is clear. I'm

163

putting a large barrier between you, the patient, and me, the doctor. That barrier doesn't matter. My knowledge will cross it. My humanity won't, because neither of us need it. Superior and Extraordinaire Consultant is very, very clued up. This man knows about hearts, but he is also very funny, in an acerbic, 'QC and barrister' sort of way. Barristers are another group of very clever people, and they also see the heart as a way of pumping blood, rather than anything to do with the emotions.

We've given up God, because He or She's unfashionable. This does leave rather a gap in human existence, as for most of our time we seem to have needed God or gods. The reality is that we haven't really given up God. We've just redefined Him, or Her. We're looking up at Mick Jagger and Elton John, Wayne Rooney, Tony Blair and so on, but they don't really work as divinities. God has actually become The Consultant. The Him or Her who has the power of life or death, like God used to do.

I'm asked to describe what happened when I had the stroke. The consultation is very short, though all the time the laser-beam eyes of the consultant are piercing me. This stroke should not have happened, I'm told. I'm a relatively young man who should have many years of decay to look forward to – my words, not his. The cause is almost certainly atrial fibrillation. I will be prescribed Flecanide to control the rhythm of my heart.

There's a strong sense that I'm NAIC, or Not An Interesting Case. I'm getting used to coming into a room where the doctor sits behind a large desk, holds a huge file in front of him or her, and looks miserably at its contents. Cue for atrial fibrillation from patient, even if

164

their problem is Irritating – or is it Irritable? – Bowel Syndrome. Doctor looks up. 'Well,' he says, with an expression of deep disappointment, 'it looks as if there's not much wrong with you.' A sense of relief flows through the patient with sufficient strength to cause a heart attack through an excess of joy.

Doctors like you to be an Interesting Case. It livens up their life no end. Brilliant consultant suggests I might consider an operation in about five years' time, if the fibrillation persists. 'It's a good operation,' he says, 'but it's not quite perfected yet.' I repress thoughts about those who, over the next five years, will presumably perfect it for me; by having it perfected on them.

The other news is that I'm to stay on Warfarin, which my GP put me on two days earlier. No drug can cure the effects of a stroke. What you're prescribed is usually a drug to thin the blood and make it less likely to clot, thereby reducing the risk of another stroke, rather than deal with the effects of the one that's just happened. Aspirin – bog basic, ordinary aspirin – has this effect. The other old stand-by is Warfarin, or rat poison. It is actually quite a dangerous drug, can have side effects, and getting the dosage right is crucial. After all, if Nature had wanted our blood thinned more than it usually is, it would have set the consistency of the blood at a lower level than normal. Warfarin and Heparin are often prescribed to those who've had an irregular heartbeat. Sometimes Dypyridamole is prescribed alongside aspirin. For those allergic to aspirin, there is a relatively new drug, Clopidogrel. As for me, I'm delighted to be on the old technology.

My consultant has not become GCSE without jumping

through the hoops, and expecting his patients to do the same. He specifies a number of medical ordeals for me to go through and report back to him. He will in turn report back to me through my GP. I'm reminded of the end of *Othello*, where the arch-villain Iago is finally exposed, condemned to death but, rather casually, sent to be tortured, before the sentence is carried out. For form's sake as much as for anything else. My torture is yet to come.

One thing worries me. I know how far I have come in a few weeks. Does he? Does he really know where I started from?

Various nasties lie in wait for me. I am told to report to another address in Harley Street, and warned I will be asked to do a little light exercise. No need to bring a change of clothes. I do manage to pack a pair of trainers.

Then I'm off. I'm still walking very slowly, and with a most uncertain ability to control direction. I pay off the taxi when I get home and instead of sauntering confidently into where I'm going, I walk into a lamp post. Very embarrassing.

I turn up to the address I have been instructed to go to, also in Harley Street, for 'tests'. I am learning that tests are what medics give you when their wife is giving them a bad time and they need to take some revenge on the patient. It then turns out that my young, male and utterly charming torturer – Australian, of course – wants me to walk and, if possible, run on a treadmill 'as hard and as long as I can manage', whilst a heart monitor is strapped to my various appendages.

I don't even have time to say that I've got a pair of trainers before I'm put on the machine, dressed in a City suit and rather nice pair of black Italian formal shoes that were unfortunately not designed for running.

Given the amount of electrics strapped to me, my biggest fear is that if I fall off, I'll be electrocuted. To find myself in effect back at the gym is something of a shock. My heart has been solid as a rock more or less ever since the stroke, strangely enough. I start to walk on the treadmill, doctor on one side, technician on the other. The technician is Australian as well. All young men and women who work in private medicine below the level of doctor are Australian, or South African. Are there *any* young people left in Australia?

'Ready to speed it up a bit?' he asks.

Fine. This is becoming a macho challenge. Like James Bond strapped on the G-force simulator, the challenge is not to push the button, slow the machine down. Slowly, the speed inches up, until I'm forced to break in to a stumbling run.

'OK?' they ask.

Wonderful, I smile through gritted teeth. Help, I think. This treadmill is going faster than the one at the gym, my lungs are starting to hurt and nasty sweat is staining my Crombie shirt. I focus down, in the only way I know to respond to physical challenge, so that the whole world consists only of my feet pounding out a rhythm on the treadmill. From somewhere in a fog of pain, sweat and searing breath, I sense the torture machine is slowing down. I pant to a standstill.

'Good,' they say. 'Your heart rhythm looks fine'.

'Brilliant,' I mutter under my breath, I'm glad one part of my bloody body has passed muster.

167

I go through various other tests, some of which, rather annoyingly, I'd been through in the summer. I trust the technicians. Often highly intelligent, they see hundreds of these tests and know intuitively when a result is out of kilter. Well, I shouldn't really say, they nod, but I'd guess that's all right.

I remember the moment in my pre-med for the cancer surgery when the technicians realised my heart was competing at Le Mans, but the engine was minus several cylinders. Their whole body language changed, their smiles stopped at the lips. 'Oh, we're sure it'll be fine,' they muttered vaguely and without any conviction.

Before I am allowed back to part-time work, I have to have my brain viewed. There's trouble fixing up an MRI scan. I am starting to fret. I am at that stage of my recovery where the desire to be back in the flow of things is at times almost as overwhelming as the illness was; yet I know I don't have the stamina.

I am cleared to drive again, a privilege denied all stroke victims for a period of time. I have served my time, and in the absence of a subsequent stroke, I am legally allowed to take the wheel again if the medics vouch for me. They do. My wife suggests I take myself, the dog and my manuscript to our home in Norfolk, the lovely bolt-hole where I do all my writing in the school holidays. I have made progress. I can walk slowly, drive a car, feed myself. My house is over the road from the school. I see it out of my study window. I am like an old war horse, scenting battle but unable to join in. I love my work, am passionate about both it and a school I love. I have a job to do and I want to be doing it. Being offered the chance to do it was one of the greatest privileges of my life. To be so near and yet so far away is not doing me good.

I drive very slowly and very carefully for the three hour journey, just to check I can still do it. On this trip, I'm the sort of driver that I'd have muttered against in the past – 'If he can't go faster than 55mph he shouldn't be on the road' – but I'm not going to take any risks. The only thing I notice is that if I take my eyes off the road at all, to adjust the radio or the cruise control, I start to steer ever so gently over to the left, just like my wayward body has been doing since the stroke, a drift which I have managed to banish from my walking. I learn not to take my eyes off the road.

We have since sold the house I went to then, and bought another one in Norfolk, though not for the obvious reasons that appear below. Our old Norfolk house dated back to the 17th century in part, but had been extensively added to in the 18th and 19th centuries. Its glory was a huge entrance hall, stone-flagged and with a staircase like a gallery on three sides, with bedrooms off it. Beyond this were more traditional, low-beamed rooms in typical Norfolk style. We loved the house, but it was not an easy place to be on one's own. We saw nothing, and heard nothing, but almost everyone who came sensed a presence in the house, not evil, but not particularly welcoming either. It was centred on a lobby area that connected the newer and the older parts of the house, and in one of the rooms up in the roof.

I stay for over a week, for most of it with only the dog as company. As always, I sense further company in the house, but it is entirely unoppressive, almost benign,

169

watchful. The manuscript of my novel comes in two parts. The first is a detailed list of comments, each linked to a page or a line, running to several pages. The second is the actual manuscript itself, with a key in the margins to link the relevant section to the editor's comment sheet. Most of the comments are minor corrections or suggestions, but there are one or two serious points. A section follows the Earl of Essex to Ireland, on his ill-fated expedition to defeat the Irish rebels. The editor thinks this section is too long, and she is right, but to shorten it has major implications for the structure of the remainder of the novel.

The editor also thinks the characterisation of the Earl of Essex is not as clear as it should be. Again, she is right. I see Essex as a deeply flawed yet utterly charismatic man, almost a cross between David Bowie and Princess Diana. He is a tragic figure, yet also an extraordinarily attractive one, and not only because of crashing good looks and high intelligence. I have not got the balance right between dominance and vulnerability, Essex as bully and Essex as villain.

My hero is a man I call Henry Gresham. I've become extraordinarily fond of Henry Gresham. I can tell you exactly where his house stood on the Strand in London, where the College he helped to refound stands in Cambridge, and show you the village where his house in Cambridge stood. I can show you the deep pool in the River Cam where he swam in the cold winter mornings and the muggy Fenland evenings. They all exist, of course, but the fictional Henry Gresham has become as real to me as all these other places. As I immerse myself in the edit, I realise more and more that Henry Gresham has something to teach me. Some pretty terrible things have happened to him, and he is faced with the easy option of giving up. Instead, without quite knowing why, he decides to fight, decides that mere survival is a virtue in itself. It's very old hat philosophically, little more than a re-hash of Stoicism with a bit more flair, but, in my present predicament, it resonates. When I created him, of course, I had no clue as to my medical future.

The week works wonders. My clumping at a keyboard – I'm determined to type out the corrections – produces a mass of errors, but the process of improvement is far faster and far more marked than it was with my handwriting. At the start of the week I'm making ten or more mistakes on each word-processed line; by the end of the week, it's a single mistake or less.

My brain seems to be working reasonably well. My first degree was in English and History, and from the start, these books have been a challenge I set myself. The challenge is to write historical crime thrillers in which the historical facts are spot-on accurate, and then to weave round actual historical truth a skein of fiction that becomes credible through the accuracy of the rest. At the same time, the narrative must somehow generate real suspense, all the tension of a conventional thriller. As a result, plotting is a nightmare, but there is also the genuine intellectual challenge of getting it right. I also love the other challenge – presenting a really surprising ending that is a massive revelation to the reader, but which, when they think back, they realise was all there for them to find, if only they'd seen it. This is even more challenging

171

when the reader knows the actual ending of the story because they know what happened or the textbooks say happened. It's never been easy to reconcile these challenges, but it's certainly no harder post-stroke, and it's just as enjoyable, rather like what I imagine the designer of a crossword puzzle might feel when he squeezes the last word into the matrix. I feel energy flowing back in to me.

There's no date for my brain scan yet. I start to worry again towards the end of the week. I suppose I should be worried about what the scan will show, but that's not it. Rather, it's that the scan is a tick in a box that might, at the end of a long list, be something that marks the end of all this, be one of the signing-off moments.

For a period I mark time. I still stick to the regime, but it's taking me less time to bounce the balls, write the letters and walk the garden, so I can feel an element of normality creeping back. I'm fretting more and more about the scan, desperate to get back to work and to some sort of routine imposed on rather than by me. I'm worried that I might enjoy this 'Life Lite' sort of existence and become hooked, not on drugs, but on being a professional convalescent.

At last I'm summoned for the MRI scan. I've been put in early in the morning, before the unit is really open. The hospital is new, the building where the scan takes place newly-painted. The waiting area is bleak. Why are doctors' and hospital waiting rooms such awful places? The only one that was even vaguely civilised was the one in Harley Street, but even that felt a little like the mortuary in a London gentleman's club.

The MRI scan is fun – Magnetic Resonance Imaging. I imagine from the name that it uses magnetic resonance to image the brain. What that actually means I don't know. I do know that The Beast is large, expensive and overbooked in hospitals, and that I should probably have had a scan rather earlier than the four or five weeks it took to arrange one.

'It can be a bit intimidating,' the nurse says. Do I want to look in The Room first to familiarise myself with It?

I find myself getting rather tart in my responses. Thank you, I say, but I am getting rather blasé about being tested, about being poked, prodded and invaded in every orifice I possess and being jammed into, onto or beside a bewildering number of shiny things that go beep and seem to cost vast amounts of money. Just get on with the damn thing.

The nurse looks hurt. I can't help thinking about The Rack, the medieval torture machine. The pain it caused was so awful that a large number of prisoners confessed all the minute the door of the torture chamber was opened and they were shown The Rack. The MRI Chamber seems to have a resonance of that. Bad joke, and bad idea to make puns inside one's own head. A sign I'm far more nervous than I want the nurse to realise.

Into changing room to don surgical gown. Oh God. Here again. At least I keep my pants on this time, and hence some dignity. I must not on any account take any metal in to The Chamber. For a moment I have an image of a deep electronic noise as fifty thousand magnets are switched on, and my body hurtles to the roof, hanging

173

there by the suddenly magnetised watch I've forgotten to take off. James Bond again.

The door has to be locked behind me, because I'm leaving valuables there. It's got to be a brave thief who robs this place.

I'm taken in to The Chamber and inserted on to a long, thin metal half-tube or tray with an apology for a mattress on top. It's like a primitive decompression chamber. Standard hospital grey paint, dim lighting. I'm told this tray will retreat, with me on it, in to the small opening behind, and I'll then be in The Machine. It will be noisy, so I'm given ear muffs. I'm a package again, and suddenly I feel depressed. I've so enjoyed not being a package this past week or so.

You must remain still, I'm told endlessly, while the scan's happening.

I'm getting used to these experiences now, and I've developed my own routine. I let my face relax, neither smiling nor frowning. I imagine that the most gloriously relaxing, warm and luxurious fluid is slowly starting to seep through my body, starting at the toes. I let the talk of the nurses to each other, and to me, wash over, leaving just a tiny bit peeping out on the surface to pick up and respond to any important instruction.

My tea tray retreats back into The Mother Ship with me on it. It is close inside The Machine, tight, hemmed in. I think I'm about to find out if I'm claustrophobic. I consider whether or not to have a screaming fit. No need; apparently, I'm not. It's really rather cosy in here. All a man needs. I have an audio link with the outside world, and a sort of mirror thing above my head which shows me nothing except another metallic bit of The Machine. If ever there was a place where in-flight movies would work, this is it. It is rather like being inside a torpedo tube. It would be claustrophobic, if I let it. I'm not going to let it.

All nursing staff have left The Chamber. The audio link asks me if I'm resting comfortably. They are going to do the first scan. It will be noisy.

It is. The nearest I can come to describing it is Cyber men playing in a steel band. Short, harsh electronic noises, with a strange rhythm and tonal differences that threaten to become almost musical but never actually do so. I'm rather enjoying this. Sudden, battering noise, then periods of relaxation. It's like being inside a nuclear reactor.

At the end of each noise session, a tinny, disembodied voice asks if I'm all right, tells me I can twitch the occasional muscle for a minute or so, and then warns me to freeze for the next session. I think up the plots for three novels.

Finally, perhaps 45 minutes later, I emerge again into the gloom of The Chamber on my little sliding tea tray. I feel strangely cleansed, as if I've been through some ritual religious experience. I begin to wonder if surgical gowns shouldn't be all white, rather than the ubiquitous rather pink, sub-Laura Ashley pattern. I'm increasingly coming to realise medicine is the new Christianity. Religious faith accepted that life on earth was crap, and the only hope was the after-life. Lose your faith in the after-life – or perhaps just lose your faith – and you're stuck with this life. Ergo, worship those people or things that prolong this, the one life you know you've got.

Hello, doctor, hello God. It can't be good for them, these doctors, being treated as God.

It's something of a relief that God isn't actually present at my MRI scan. Him or Her, the Giver of Life, can sometimes confuse things by Their Magnificence.

The Technician, on the other hand, has both her feet firmly on the ground. She, as some ancient incantation might sound, is not God, like John the Baptist. She is simply The Messenger To God. And, rather like John the Baptist, if she gets it wrong it will be her head served up on a cheap plate.

Rather than being worried by all this, she smiles at me.

'Ever had trouble wearing a hat?' she says.

Well, as it happens, I have. When I was a Reserve Officer in the Royal Navy, the only hats I could cram on my head were so big that the white bit on the top overhung my head like trees shading a lovers' glade.

'You've got a cyst on the right side of your brain,' she says. 'Bigger than a very large walnut. I guess it's been there since birth. Your skull's grown round it.'

'That would explain it,' one of my brothers says months later as I tell him this story. Both my older brothers have been lovely during my illness, visiting, ringing up and showing genuine care. This one is a doctor, and it's been invaluable having his advice.

'Explain what?' I ask. I'm told a story I've never heard before. When as a new-born baby, I was brought in to see my Aunty Mary, herself a GP, she shrieked and said, 'Take that baby away! It's got a funny shaped head!' Apparently this story was deemed fit only to be circulated among the medical members of our family, and not told to the head's owner.

The final hurdle is the neurologist. You get sent to one of those so he or she can reassure your employers that you won't start whistling Dixie in the middle of a Board meeting, go into sudden long dark teatimes of the soul and, to use the technical terms, that you haven't lost your marbles and there's still someone in residence upstairs.

I find out what the neurologist will ask me to do. Why? One of my favourite stories is from the original *Star Trek* series. As a trainee officer, Captain James T. Kirk is sent in to the Simulator as Captain of a Star Ship. Except it is a mission that he can never win. The computer has seen to it that whatever the trainee does, the mission will fail and the Klingons will blow up the Star Ship. Captain Kirk is the only trainee ever to have won the mission. How? He steals in the night before and changes the computer programme. As with Starship Command, so with the medical profession. Know your enemy. Or, at the very least, ask as many of them as are willing, exactly what a neurologist will ask a patient to do in the aftermath of a stroke to see if said patient is up to returning to work. And plan accordingly.

The neurologist might want to stop me going back to work. He will ask me to stand on one leg, I am told by my medical spy in the camp. I have never been able to stand on one leg. There is an immediate addition to my training schedule, 15 minutes standing on one leg every day. Except that I can never get it to much more than seven seconds.

The neurologist is a lovely man, as it turns out. He is

near retirement, and ever-so-slightly tired in what, strangely, is rather a reassuring way. I know he could kill my career. He knows he could kill my career. He still manages to be extraordinarily kind and wise, without any loss of professional standards. I manage to push when I should push, pull when I should pull and stand, for a short time, on one leg.

After it's all over, he says, 'Come and look at the scan.'

The picture is pasted up on an illuminated screen, just like an X-ray. It's quite disturbing seeing a picture of your own brain. He shows me the cyst. It's big, and he clearly has some admiration and respect for it, particularly as he too thinks it's been there since birth. He shows me two or three black spots on the pictures.

'That's where the stroke hit you,' he says, 'view them as burnt-out circuits. They can also, of course, be a sign of multiple sclerosis.'

My ears pick up. 'Do I have MS?' I hear myself saying.

'No,' he says, 'I don't think so. But there's one more thing I'd like to ask you to do.'

My heart sinks. I hadn't realised just how much I don't want to go through more tests, see more doctors. Haven't I done my bit? How many more hoops must I jump through? Can't I just be left to get on with the rest of whatever my life will be?

'I know,' says the neurologist, and I really think he does, 'I know how much you must want to get this all over with. But you're basically a healthy man. We think it was atrial fibrillation that caused the stroke, but the danger is that if there seems to be an easy, obvious answer we overlook a deeper underlying cause. I just want to be sure, before we sign you off, to look under every stone. See, here...'

He points to the picture. 'There are two arteries that supply most of the blood to the brain. Your left-hand one is fine. The right-hand one I'm just not sure about. The scan hasn't quite caught it. It could be OK. It could be smaller than normal, but within permissible limits. That happens quite a lot, and sometimes the other side enlarges to compensate. Or it could be smaller than it should be, and, as such, might have caused your stroke. If that's the case, there are various procedures we can undertake to open it out. But there's another procedure that'll tell us for certain if it's too small or not.'

Do they tell doctors in training to use 'us' and not 'me'? It has a magical affect on the delivery of the message. When 'us' comes in to it, the Doctor As God suddenly vanishes. Suddenly, we're in this together, doctor and patient. It's a team effort.

'I ought to tell you one thing. There's a very slight prospect that this procedure can cause another stroke.'

'Would you have it done if you were me?' I ask.

'Yes,' says the consultant simply.

'Then there's no argument, is there?' I say.

I have made myself forget the name of this procedure, but then again this diary was never written as a medical textbook. I know it required a local anaesthetic, a large number of needles and a truly historic, huge black bruise on my thigh (thinks: quite a long way from the heart?) that seemed to move through my body and stayed with me for weeks. And an overnight stay in hospital, presumably to check I didn't have that second stroke.

The private hospital is very different from the NHS ward. It is clean, quiet and the food is wonderful. The staff seem pleased as punch to be working there.

The result comes back clear. Whatever it is they have done to me has shown a normal-size pipe supplying blood to the brain.

Now that I have been passed, I am allowed back to a limited amount of work: mornings or afternoons only, no evenings and no weekends. I miss supporting the school sport hugely, so regular and fixed a part of my life as it has been for 35 years. People are very kind, my PA, in particular, taking a very firm line with me and booting me out of the door in a tone that brooks no disobedience when I have worked my half day.

Few people know what was wrong with me. I sail along for a morning or an afternoon like a man rejuvenated. Never has the walk up the drive seemed so refreshing, or life so inherently exciting. I reach the front door of my home all smiles and cheerfulness, and then find myself waking up three hours later.

I still struggle to sign my name as I used to, topping and tailing letters by hand. For the moment, I allow the 'Dear Mr and Mrs Smith' bit to be typed, along with the 'Yours sincerely'. We'll get rid of that soon enough, I vow grimly, and do half an hour's writing by hand every night before I go to bed. I hide my weaker, left hand in my trouser pocket. It tends to droop a little. Perhaps only I realise this. Not true. My wife realises. She was the one who told me. I realise anew what an appalling battering the body takes in a stroke, and listen to the final judgment. Though I am seemingly in

180

good health, it will take up to a year to be back to full strength.

Nuts, I think. Six months maximum. Six months from the time of the stroke, October 5th 2005, *not* six months from the time I'm told it will take a year. I return to full-time work in January. The only concession I am prepared to make is that I resign from various external Governorships and Boards. If I get tired, my speech slurs, but I can now develop strategies to recognise what is happening, and correct myself.

By the end of the Easter term my signature and my writing are back to normal, and my typing reaches (or peaches) the same level of inaccuracy as it always managed. I no longer need to hide my left hand. I need the Easter holiday, but when I come back from it, it is almost as if the stroke had never happened.

Almost?

Energy levels are good. The handwriting is indistinguishable from what it was before, but only I know it takes that little bit extra effort to get it right. I suspect a policeman who has looked down the barrel of a gun is never quite the same again. I looked down the barrel of a medical gun, and I will never be the same again. Yet never being the same again is sometimes a good thing. I have a new zest for life, a new pleasure in the simplest of things: walking, talking, writing, typing.

Epilogue

In the confusion that surrounds an illness, I had remembered reading that only 10% of stroke victims made a full recovery. My reading took place well after that recovery had taken place. It took my family to put the record straight. Reading the proofs of this book they confirmed what I had forgotten. It was the hospital that told me the 10% figure, which I passed on rather glumly to my wife and children at the time.

As a teacher I have always believed that the cruellest thing of all is to set limits on a child. The children tell you what they can do, and the teacher's job is not to limit ambition to sensible proportions, but to help unleash what is innate within the child. Please, William, stop writing about this strange man called Hamlet; I asked for and want an essay on What I Did In My Holidays. This Theory of Relativity stuff is all fine and well, but will it get you a job? You do realise, Laurence/Julia/Marlon, that a career in acting will never pay the mortgage?

Perhaps the medics could learn a little from the teachers. Of course any sensible doctor has to tell the patient desperate to live that talking to a tree, wearing a crystal or drinking bat's blood will not provide a miracle cure. Yet where there is a chance of recovery, it is not an act of kindness to tell the patient, even by implication, that statistically speaking they will not do it.

My illness did leave me wondering, if in an age where medical science has been revolutionised by the machine, we have not tended to overlook the mind.

It also left me certain that I would not have made a full recovery without the unflinching support of my wife, my children and my employer.